THE WILD DROVER

A
JACK RUTHERFORD
ADVENTURE

Published in paperback in 2019 by Sixth Element Publishing
on behalf of Ken Braithwaite

Sixth Element Publishing
Arthur Robinson House
13-14 The Green
Billingham TS23 1EU
Tel: 01642 360253
www.6epublishing.net

ISBN 978-1-912218-51-6

British Library Cataloguing in Publication Data. A catalogue record for this book is
available from the British Library.

Cover illustration by Vanessa Wells.

Printed in Great Britain.

THE WILD DROVER

A
JACK RUTHERFORD
ADVENTURE

KEN BRAITHWAITE

DEDICATION

Doreen and all our family have been wonderfully
supportive and most encouraging. And thank you to
Nathan Braithwaite and Jeff Auty.

Gillie Hatton and Graeme Wilkinson
at Sixth Element have proved their high repute.

Don, Barbara.

with my best wishes.

Ken,

CONTENTS

CHAPTER 1
ATTACK ON STAINMORE

Through the early morning mist I can see one of them stalking me and the other one will doubtless be on horseback trailing me and taking advantage of the grey mist.

Moving onward, the mist swirled as a gentle breeze eventually materialised, trees appeared in the foreground now and birdsong. That would soon cease as we continued the long slow climb out of Brough and headed for the open moor.

As arranged, we'd left Brough, my hometown, in the very early morning. The town is a major staging route across the North of England and up to sixty coaches arrive and leave with all the attendant noise of horses neighing, men shouting, passengers yelling and pandemonium ensuing. This all at something like 4.30am to ensure the coaches arrive in York on time. I had no intention of this noise affecting my drove of cattle and moved my small work force very quickly into action.

An early morning start was vital and by 6am I had roused my men from their slumbers in the drovers' rest house and we set off for the holding ground, known as a stance.

Collecting the cattle from this overnight field, we moved slowly through the streets that were covered in a thick early autumn mist, trees dripping moisture on our necks. There was at first no breeze and a grey foreboding appearance to the whole of the now briefly silent town as we took the path along the drove road to cross the bleak Stainmore heights.

This route is the difficult and dangerous high road across the Pennines to our overnight stance at Bowes and then ultimately to Scotch Corner and beyond.

Frankly, if I was in the villain's shoes I would wait until we reached the higher ground before attacking, that way there would be fewer witnesses.

My name is Jack Rutherford, aged twenty and with a short history of droving, trouble making and mayhem behind me. I stand six feet tall, lean, fit and with a tendency to work hard and play hard. Exiled to Scotland for three years by my Father, I spent that time raiding after cattle thieves and dealing with their savage ways in a similar manner. I was not exactly unprepared for what was about to happen and I had one very strong advantage in my huge Irish Wolfhound, Dag, who was a known killer.

Brough lies in a valley below the mass that is Stainmore Moor and a regular path leads between occasional stone walls ever climbing towards the grey misty moor that appears momentarily as we move steadily forward. Cattle make a steady pace, grazing by the wayside when possible and constant attention is needed to maintain a gentle but regular rhythm. It is some twelve miles from Brough to the next major stopping place, Bowes, and I had no intention of being on the moors at nightfall. Summer means short nights and long days with intense heat lower down in the valley but easing a little as we reach higher ground.

Climbing steadily, the herd became strung out along the way, moving into single file at narrow points and spreading out as far as they dare when the path widened.

Once above four hundred feet the moorland proper begins and with my Top Man Duncan Brooks leading, we traced the route across the open rough countryside which slowly became more apparent as a small breeze swirled the mists away.

Drovers must be over thirty years of age and married. Duncan fulfils this role but is fond of the beer and keeps failing. I retain him and keep him sober when he is with me.

Dag, my dog, had quietly disappeared at the first sign of possible conflict and at this very moment he was stalking the man on horseback who I had glimpsed briefly as both he and his companion had taken the opportunity to move in much closer while the weather was poor.

Our cattle moved steadily on with Duncan at the head and two or three young hands either side of the beasts and me bringing up the rear. Strangely an extra person had appeared that morning but knowing I was shorthanded the crew would let me know who had joined at our first rest stop.

Gently lowing, grazing as they moved, the cattle gave off that familiar smell I will always associate with droving, a mixture of warm heat and bovine stink.

My very large bunch of black cattle and their herdsmen had now spread out along the moorland path brushing aside the heather and bracken that intrudes across the road.

We were still climbing steadily to a particular spot I wished to reach, and there the attack could commence for I was on familiar ground. None of my men were aware of the danger lurking behind us. I kept that to myself and was content for the crew to move steadily onward.

I was anxiously waiting for nothing less than the massive bog that festered on the moor top, avoided by countless drovers before me; it was a known hazard to those who used these very exposed and rough uplands.

Slowly and steadily the robbers crept ever forward, making use of the limited sparse cover as soldiers do, but strangely never looking back, a bad mistake.

From my vantage point I watched them come forward. I had open rough moorland to my left and falling ground to my right in a south west direction.

Their best possible point of attack was about two hundred yards further on but that did not fit with my own plans. I moved into the body of my cattle and walked like this for some good distance before I deemed it just right for an attack then I slowed down to let the cattle move forward and away from me and the coming noisy conflict.

Both cutthroats moved in quickly for their attack and they raced across the ground to confront me.

My dog and I work very well together with an almost unnerving knowledge of the needs of each, honed to perfection by our long hours tending the cattle.

He had stalked the man on horseback for over a mile. I saw nothing of him as he'd crept along, keeping very low on his haunches and out of sight. I had to place absolute reliance on his presence for this plan to work.

At my whistle, Dag became the savage hunter that I had witnessed only once before.

He broke quickly into his huge stride, leapt from cover and attacked the rider on horseback, pulled him to the ground and ripped his throat out in one ferocious savage movement.

This man's piercing death screams unnerved the other robber who had leapt forward very quickly to try to overpower me, waving a vicious long sword.

All my frustrations brought me to the fight with a wild anger and a determination to finish this matter once and for all. Red mists again.

With a long knife in one hand and a stout stave in the other, I waited whilst he glanced around at his mate's death screams and then I fell on him. I slashed at his throat and he went down but he was not badly wounded and moved quickly into a defensive stance. I attacked him again, quickly, but tripped on a grass tussock.

He used that moment to try stomp on my outflung leg but I twisted quickly and kicked his knee joint as I fell. We both dropped to the ground. I hit my head and was briefly dizzy. He tried to knife me in the large artery inside my leg but again I twisted away and took a heavy slash above my knee. Blood pouring from my leg, I struggled to remain upright using my stout stave as an arm prop.

We fought furiously back and forth, both wounded and bleeding, now on the ground, now standing trading blows. That sword intrigued me. I noticed that it was weighty and very well used but now growing heavy in his hand.

Being a former soldier now in Kirk's employ he was a very capable fighter and although badly hurt on his knee that I had kicked, he swung repeatedly at me with the wicked sword.

We struggled back and forth but I was aware of him tiring quickly, and I needed a quick result before I lost more blood.

Using the very last of my strength I took my stave, reached out and pushed at his chest to separate us and in a desperate gamble threw my knife straight toward him, losing my main weapon.

It went straight through his heart and he dropped heavily, gasped and coughed then died as his heart failed him.

Absolutely drained from the fight and a loss of blood, I slumped to the ground, exhausted beyond measure by the battle and passed out.

Coming to briefly I saw in the far distance the herd moving steadily on without me. Not taking my herdsmen in to my confidence was now proving a very costly mistake. I was alone and seriously injured.

I also had some very immediate problems, mainly two men, now corpses, known to be in my whereabouts and me unable to move from my heavily bleeding wound and complete dizziness.

Dag's appearance gave me great encouragement and he whimpered beside me and licked my face, but a fat lot of good that did.

At the sound of somebody approaching, I kept as quiet as I could and bade Dag to remain silent. We watched and waited very much on edge when I heard a voice quietly calling my name, "Jack, Jack."

Dag remained still and quiet until a figure came towards me out of the heather.

The figure had the appearance of a slightly built young man with a very concerned expression.

"Jack, Jack," the soft voice said again and through my hazy stupor I recognised the accent. Could it really be Giselle, my damsel in distress?

So that's who the extra hand was that I had noted when we started out this morning. It was Giselle wearing men's clothing and her hair tucked carefully under her cap.

Could it be she was trying to be with me?

My confused and battered brain just could not take in this change of fate. How could the one girl I longed to see again be here for my help and actually calling my name?

No wonder Dag was so relaxed about the newcomer. He, like me, thought she was just fine. Had she secretly come back to find me?

But to see me in this condition… I tried to rise but failed and fell back as Giselle came towards me out of the heather and knelt by my side, quickly examining my wound. Her expression on seeing the massive cut above my knee made me more aware than ever of my predicament. Immediately she tore strips of cloth from the boy's shirt she was wearing and cleaned and started to dress my cut in a very competent way. I tried to speak but she 'shushed' me and continued to bind my wound.

She then raised my head, lifted my eyelid to examine me and my face and proclaimed, in a broken English, "You av concussion but your wound is on the surface and you bleedin' very much."

I knew that but was so very grateful for her concern.

There was now a reaction to the battle and I felt an overwhelming need to rest and sleep.

There was a constant pain in my head and I could sense I was about to faint. Confused memories came flooding back as I fell to the heather. Black Cattle, Dumfries, dangerous enemies. Brough.

It all began way, way back before Dumfries…

CHAPTER 2
WILD DAYS, SCOTLAND

For three years I was banished to the Highlands of Scotland by my Father for a catalogue of misdemeanours that came to a head when I released two massive boar pigs into the crowded Market Place in Brough under Stainmore, my home town. Amongst other things, Brough was a major stopping point for coaches travelling from London to Edinburgh and as many as eight vehicles could be on the main thoroughfare of the town at any time. There are changes of horses and wheels to attend to quickly, whilst the local hostelries provide overnight accommodation for weary travellers and warm drinks for those stretching their weary legs.

There is a weekly market with stalls all along the main street which is thronged with wives buying fresh produce, men selling wares, tinkers selling pots and pans, or it was until my boars arrived. They left the place in a rare shambles when they'd finished, stalls overturned, fruit, eggs and vegetables flying in all directions, pots and pans all over and a wagon wheel smashed by the raging boars.

When the excitable pigs were eventually cornered, my name was bandied about.

Father picked up a huge bill for damages and sent me to Scotland with a very cantankerous friend of his.

At fifteen years of age, I went to Killin on the shores of Loch Tay and learned the droving trade the hard way. That involved me in cattle raising, animal welfare, the use of the dirk as a weapon and when our stock was stolen, a long hard chase over moorland and a hard battle with the thieves. That was when I killed a man who flew at me with a massive broadsword, not a nice experience at seventeen years of age but I had grown a lot by then, very tall, fit and healthy and well able to take care of myself after my constant run ins with my Guardian.

Brough under Stainmore, in Westmorland, was a wonderful place to be brought up in, a very busy market town with seventeen inns or taverns for the many grooms and the horses pulling carriages from Scotland along the main road to England via Scotch Corner and then South to York and London.

As a small boy I gazed in wonder at these magnificent coach and four horse vehicles, their snorting horses, grooms rushing hither and thither and passengers alighting for a hurried walk and tea or beer before the horn was blown loudly, and all rejoined for the next stage.

Our schoolteacher Miss Hutchinson told us that the passengers leaving that evening at eleven o'clock would be in York by 4am and in London the next day.

School was interesting and sometimes painful. I had the habit of getting into mischief and was strapped frequently by both the teacher and my Father when he became aware of my misdeeds.

To me it had seemed a good idea tie up all the doors on the school and trap everybody inside. I was caned with six of the best!

My idea of a firework or two among the horses and grooms created quite an unusual fuss. Father thrashed me good and hard and banned me from going out for a week. And caned again!

Ladies' bloomers that I put on the Market Cross caused the Mayor to issue Father a stern warning about my wild 'goings on'.

Damming up the little Swindale Beck late one evening seemed a good prank but it went awry and apparently filled the cellars of the Castle Inn and the Old Fleece with a good head of water. I don't think I have ever seen grown men so cross and although then I was only eleven years old I was given a very severe beating by Father in front of these two men who have been reluctant to talk to me until very recently.

Despite all these side issues, school became enjoyable because it slowly dawned on me that I wanted to follow my Father and become a drover. My brothers and sisters had all left home for jobs in other towns and cities but the cattle trade held a continuing fascination for me, probably coming from the wonderful sounding places that both Father described and that were mentioned by the grooms when they called their carriage destinations.

Watching Dad I realised the importance of counting accurately and being able to write it down, which meant reading and so I left school at fourteen years old with a good school report. Instantly I was involved in our farming and droving business, moving cattle, cleaning out the byres and the drovers' accommodation, cutting firewood, mending fences and meeting the drovers on the way in to Brough to suggest our accommodation and overnight cattle stance was superior to any other.

Father was expected back from a drove with cattle to York and some dim soul had placed two enormous pigs in a temporary sty beneath my bedroom window. They turned out to be boars, intent on fighting and their snorting and grunting, squealing and shuffling kept me awake most of the night.

In my defence I was exhausted and had only reached my bedroom at 11pm after waiting in vain for drovers to appear from the North and I was really tired from my day's labours. But sleep would not come, the row was intense and the din was all on my side of the house. Twice I got up and shouted at the silly pigs, but they only kept silent until I put my candle out and then started again.

This was a Market Day which I completely forgot in my intense anger at those boars and the imbeciles who had left them and, giving it little thought, I turned the noisy fractious things loose early the next day to try and get some sleep.

To my incredible dismay they chose not to go in to our meadow but to head off at great speed into Market Street and of course it was Market Day. By the time I had rushed over all the damage was done.

Every market stall was on its side, people were running away in alarm from these stupid pigs who by now were festooned with market cloths, stall coverings and even some bunting.

My heart sank. This was a catastrophe and all my making.

It took me and many others two hours to catch those damned pigs and secure them again. Then the questions started and there was no way out. I had to confess everything was my fault. The Mayor and Council were summoned, I was arrested and put under lock and key to await my Father's return.

Two whole days I stayed in that room. Food was brought and a bucket for sanitary purposes but no visits from anybody. All I could hear was loud lamentations to the Mayor and a rising bill of costs that filled me with deep dread.

Father returned on the third day and visited the Mayor where they spent two hours discussing the whole episode, costs and my punishment. It appears there was a very considerable amount of wrangling about the amounts involved. I should have known, Dad was a very astute man where money was concerned and every effort was made to reduce the bill to its lowest ebb.

It still came to £23.11s.4d. A huge amount and bless me, Dad paid it.

His cold hard anger distressed me more than I can say. He didn't beat me as I expected. I was completely ignored.

My nerves were on edge and I was fraught with fear and actually trembling. To be so dismissed by my own Father was beyond my belief and the enormity of what I had done now sank in.

This anger meant something was in the offing, something which I would not like and sure enough it happened. Dougal MacPherson, a Scottish drover, came in two nights later and was greeted by Father as his true friend from years back. They went into deep conversation for many hours with occasional glances in my direction.

Mum had tried to comfort me but Dad would have none of it, which made her cry a lot.

I slept uneasy in my bed each night after doing all my chores and although I was fed, it was a very cold house with no conversation and no loving gestures from Mum.

I learnt next morning that my fate was sealed. I was banished to Scotland for three years and would be moving out immediately with Dougal to stay in the Highlands.

I'd heard tales about Dougal MacPherson, who was a very hard man, a drover of high renown and a ferocious fighter and warrior.

As soon as we set off that day, we quarrelled and in retrospect it was deliberate on his part. Within five miles of Brough on the way to Penrith, we had our first fisticuffs and all the stories were correct. Although he was only about 5'6" tall he was a bastard in a fight. I was fifteen years old then and about 5'9" high but growing and used to many a scrap but it was nothing to the beating I got from that cantankerous old drover. My first lesson in survival, Scottish style.

It was early October 1814 in foul weather when Dougal and I walked to Penrith in a state of open warfare. Fists, boots, sticks all rained on my head at strange intervals. But I learnt. I learnt to anticipate when he would attack and created a defensive strategy based on my fleetness of foot but that gradually adapted into a rapid retreat to recover and attack.

The first time I tried this I failed, but I saw a different light in his brown eyes that was almost satisfaction. Penrith came and went, various stops were made on our journey and battle continued but with each confrontation I learnt defence and vicious savage attack. Plus I got to know the old devil. He had no family but a loving wife Peggy and they lived on a small farm in Killin, way up in the Highlands of Scotland. Dougal was forty five years old, a former Scottish soldier in the Black Watch Regiment and had fought in Europe under the Duke of Wellington but missed out on Waterloo. He had been a Sergeant in the Regiment and was justifiably proud of his military service.

An observer would see a man in heavy boots, leggings, serge trousers, a long waistcoat and jacket, and a face gnarled brown with the outdoor life style. Short black hair under a Scots bonnet and a look carved from granite, brown eyes that missed nothing and clean shaven.

Each evening he would guide us to a drovers' lodgings

which were basic but sufficient, warm, with a fairly comfortable bed and simple food.

I could only surmise that Dougal was carrying a lot of money to pay back the Promissary Notes he had given when he purchased his cattle and this kept him always on the alert for thieves and robbers known to be in the area as we neared Carlisle.

Our accommodation that night was in the Drove Inn in Rickergate, Carlisle and although it said 'wines' above the door, it was mild beer and a pie we wanted as we entered. It seems Father had given money to Dougal for my costs on this epic journey which I had to pay back from my earnings in the Highlands.

Two mild beers were pulled and meat pie was suggested and ordered. We made our way in to a corner where we could watch the comings and goings in the tavern. It was a low smoke filled room with six other people in a group at the other end of the room and when our meal arrived, we quietly ate and watched.

After a period of steady drinking by the other party, who must have sent out a message, three men came in and looked carefully round until, through the smoke, they saw us in the corner.

Dougal watched them and silently nudged me and indicated their presence which I had already seen. He whispered, "They're serious trouble and after my money."

His choice of the corner seats had been a good defensive strategy. They could approach from the front and two only could attack.

I whispered, "We're in this together," which received a wry look and a snort of contempt. That did it, as doubtless it was intended to do and I bristled at his low opinion of my ability as a fighter.

The three men came and stood in front of us and asked, outright, that Dougal give them all his money, or else.

My foot came round and caught the nearest man on his left knee which collapsed and he fell but not before I had caught him under his throat and he gagged as he went down.

Dougal had wasted no time and his attack on the next man was truly unbelievable. He became a raging tornado and with feet, teeth, arms and legs, he practically devoured the ruffian who fell, a bleeding mess.

My predicament was the huge thief who now stood in front of me swinging aggressively and roaring like a bull. I sidestepped as best I could but took a very heavy painful blow to my face and I staggered, but before I could recover, a veritable demon took over and Dougal smashed this huge man to the ground with scientific precision and mangled him on the floor.

Absolute silence ensued in that room. The drinkers looked abashed, embarrassed and wishing to help and eventually the moaning and crying of our assailants brought the other occupants of the room to their feet and ropes were passed round the three thugs. Constables were summoned and the three led away to the town dungeons.

We deemed it prudent to quietly pay our dues and leave

as unobtrusively as possible, certain in the knowledge that the other drovers in that room would keep very quiet.

At the Scotch Arms Hotel nearby we found accommodation for the night and next morning, very early we were on our way.

Through Gretna, Annan, Lockerbie, Romano Bridge, Couldstaneslap, Uphall and Falkirk. We made on average twenty miles a day and by late October we came upon Falkirk and it was there that Dougal had to clear all his debts on Letters of Credit.

As drovers we buy cattle at market, or from farmers for an agreed price and then give a percentage down in cash as a token of a debt. We further give a Letter of Credit for the balance of the money agreed on sale payable in three months from the sale date. For instance if Dougal bought 100 stolts or cattle from a farmer for £5.10s.0d he would owe him £550.00. If the farmer agrees they can then negotiate a percentage down and the balance due in, normally, three months. This gives the farmer instant cash and the drover time to take the cattle to market and make, hopefully, a profit.

Reputations rise and fall on the strength of a drover's Letter of Credit and prompt payment brings cash for the long winter.

Dougal made immediate contact with all his customers and fulfilled his obligations. It is not unknown for the drover to be out of profit as the margins can be very small.

Then we set off for Killin, where we arrived to a warm welcome from Peggy, Dougal's wife, who took me in and treated me with such affection over time that I became almost her son that never was.

Over the next three years I learned the ways of the drover, hard winters, spring round-ups of sheep for shearing, cattle to tend and care for and robbing rotten thieves.

Dougal instilled in me a love of the countryside and coupled that with a clear knowledge of the dangers always lurking in those remote Scottish hills. Apart from a few sheep, the principal income to the farm came from rearing and selling cattle and in the wide open fields the condition of the beasts could be readily assessed by any passer-by, including cattle rustlers. For this reason we kept a watchful eye on strangers who were actively discouraged from lingering in our vicinity.

But inevitably thieves came who regularly attempted and indeed succeeded once in stealing twelve of our cattle. I was seventeen years of age then, well developed and capable of holding my own against any local youths and some grown men who questioned my ability. They didn't repeat their taunts.

We arranged for our reduced herd to be cared for through neighbours and then we left on our mission.

Dougal and I stalked them for two whole days before they let their guard down and I'm ashamed to say we killed all four and left them where they fell in a very remote spot.

Rumours abounded locally but we kept absolutely silent and so far nothing has come of that matter.

Three years is a long time to be away from home but I stuck it out and welcomed the letters my Mother wrote and I know she welcomed my replies which of course took simply ages to arrive, usually with the pack horse men.

Dougal called me to the fireside from my studies one evening and asked me to sit. We talked at considerable length about my development and ambitions and eventually, with Peggy's agreement came to the conclusion I should now make my way back to England and consider my future career.

It was with a very heavy heart that I left Dougal and Peggy. They had been a huge influence in my development, insisting that I continue to read and study as much as possible and those long nights reading by the light of a flickering candle still stay in my mind.

But home I came in the May of 1818 and was welcomed by Father, and my Mother cried at my change from young man to adult and made a lovely fuss of me.

CHAPTER 3
DAG THE WOLFOUND AND DUMFRIES MARKET

You've heard me talk about this great wolfhound I tolerate and this may be a good moment to hear how we met.

Early September on a bright warm day, a huge flock of geese had come through Brough on the way to York Market. They were driven by wild Irish drovers, by their looks a very mean crowd of men.

They shared no information with anybody, which was most unusual, all drovers brought tales of happenings elsewhere and were our principle means of news and gossip from far and wide.

But not these Irish ruffians. Heads down and eyes averted they were people to avoid. Passing through some people had bought the odd goose but the prices were high and sales were few, the birds being in poor condition from their long journey from Ireland.

Geese create a lot of noise and we had a herd of cattle in a steading some distance away, high in the hills for safety.

Father asked me to check them out and very early the

next morning following the passage of the geese, I walked to our steading to see if there had been any disturbance from rustling.

Leaving the town I enjoyed the fresh gentle breeze, early morning sunshine and with a light heart I stepped out on the hard climb. Thankfully the cattle were settled down, peacefully chewing the cud and there appeared to be none missing, but this was an opportunity to walk round the herd and check the animals furthest away.

I am very familiar with this area having grown up here before going to Scotland and anything slightly out of the ordinary is to be investigated, particularly as cattle are valuable and a prime target for the cattle thieves.

Mindful of the appearance of the Irish drovers and their reputation I was particularly watchful. Below the cattle field and in gorse bushes and low trees, something caught my eye.

Cattle thieves are a very rough and ready crowd, often having deserted soldiers in their midst and mixing with them, from my Scottish experience, can be a death sentence.

Very cautiously I moved round the herd in the direction of the bushes where the disturbance seemed to be, all the time on the look out for an ambush.

I carried a strong stick with me, as always, but no other weapon and felt exposed, but the welfare of the herd came first and any hidden thief had to be dealt with very severely. Creeping forward, my senses alert, I came upon a huge bundle of fur and assumed it was a dead calf of ours.

Closer inspection revealed the carcass of a huge dog and I had to get it removed quickly before the cattle smelt it and became agitated and unmanageable.

Then I realised there was a very large knife or dagger thrust through the dog's front leg and deeply embedded in the tree it was lying under.

Looking round and keeping very quiet, I was convinced I was alone.

Moving slowly I grasped the dagger and with very extreme effort removed it from the tree and the dog's leg. What a magnificent animal he must have been.

Very big boned but now failing sinew and muscle. I stared in horror at the fate that had befallen the huge animal and prepared to move it. Nearby I knew there was a steep bank with gorse and bramble bushes at the bottom and well away from our herd. That was the spot to dispose of this huge carcass.

As I moved to pick up the dog, it gave a small sound, not a growl, a low whine.

Surprise, surprise. Not dead!

That put me in a real dilemma because despite being a long way from home and alone, there was now a sick animal to tend.

I stroked the dog's face very gently to test for a reaction and its eyelids quivered. Could I save this dog? Goodness me, it would not be for the want of trying, I resolved. Using my hat, I ran downhill to the small beck I was aware of and collected some clean fresh water.

Small dribbles of this I allowed into the dog's mouth

and after a long hour there were signs of life and activity. I took off my serge coat, covered the dog with that and made him, definitely a him, comfortable with dry bracken to lie on.

Slowly over the next fifteen minutes he became more active, at one point licking my hand but making very small movements. It was then I saw the massive weals on his side from a whip or metal bar. He had been very savagely beaten.

More and more small amounts of water were poured down his throat and I started to clean his wounds with a torn piece of my shirt, hoping Mother would understand as it was the only one I had.

Thinking about it, this dog probably followed or belonged to the Irish drovers as it had the appearance of a similar magnificent one I had seen elsewhere. They are a very big breed of dog.

Food became the next priority. I made the wound as comfortable as I could and set off for home. Once there I begged some small scraps of bread and some oats to make into a form of porridge. I explained to my Mother and Father what I was about when I reported on the state of the herd. Father was pleased with my report but cautioned me as to the wild savage nature of Irish Wolfhounds as we now assumed this dog was. He particularly stressed their inability to herd cattle.

After a long hard walk back, I came to the dog and after giving him a little more water offered him some food.

I was agreeably surprised that despite being desperately hungry, he took the offering from my hands most gently, no snatching which I thought was a good start.

Over the next three hours I fed him and tended his wounds and at the end of that time he struggled to his feet. His condition was even worse when standing, huge bleeding wounds to his side and a big cut where the dagger had held him to the tree. Obviously he had made very strenuous efforts to escape.

From my experience with dogs, they can withstand a considerable amount of hardship and pain when working but this was beyond all my belief.

Once stood, though shaking, he would not leave my side, it must have taken one and a half hours to walk the two miles downhill to my house. There I put him in an outhouse on a bed of straw and he collapsed into a deep sleep.

My Father and I spoke about this matter for many hours that night. We are both drovers, me in the early stages of the business and though I had no dog of my own, relying on our family collies mostly, an Irish Wolfhound was the last creature to muster cattle with.

Next morning my Father suggested we check the area the dog was found in, just out of curiosity and on arrival we cast about in increasing circles and after ten to fifteen minutes I was called over to view the carcasses of two huge Ganders. They had been killed by having their necks bitten through. Feathers lying about gave some indication of the struggle that had taken place.

After a further search we found marks on the ground of a squabble and more feathers.

We both thought long and hard about this and came to the reluctant conclusion that the huge dog had not belonged to the Irish drovers but rather was trailing them and had taken two very big and valuable Ganders for food. They must have followed, caught the dog and dealt with him.

This would account for the drovers' anger and surly behaviour when passing through Brough, particularly if they thought the dog was local.

I was in a quandary. I'd saved the beast only to find now that I had nursed and nurtured a known killer.

To explain, my Father was not only a drover and successful farmer but attached to our house was a small stone building we used to provide very basic accommodation and meals for passing drovers.

Nearby we owned a damp, enclosed meadow that was particularly useful for an overnight stance for droving cattle passing along the routes. From this we earned a very steady income.

Here, because of the very good pasture from the moist conditions cattle could remain overnight in a secure field before moving on.

This gave Mr and Mrs Rutherford, my parents, the extra income they needed to support the large house and property.

I have three brothers and three sisters, me being the youngest and although they have all left home now, we still maintain that welcome stop over for Father's various friends in the droving business

I'd named this dog Dag for no other reason than that I'd found him with a dagger in his front foot.

I've kept both the dog and the dagger.

Dag was inseparable from me now and with very great reluctance I roped him and took him with us to the cattle stance that particular morning to introduce him to the beasts and watch his reaction to them.

My Father made it very clear he was against the whole idea, the dog's reputation now very well known and he was considered a dangerous liability.

Walking to the cattle, the dog took a great interest in his surroundings, particularly all our other dogs but he appeared to be very proud to be in my company. I watched him very carefully as we approached the herd, there was no reaction but a keen interest.

My task was to move gently along the edge of the large stance and encourage the herd to the road exit for the drovers to commence the day's travel. It is essential that the cattle are kept docile and calm to have a good start to the drove. Dag behaved very well, a keen eye on the stolts as they are called, but no lunging or barking and on one occasion when a feisty bull attempted to charge at me he stood his ground, made a deep throated growl and the bull backed off. I was quite pleased at the brief performance and against my own instincts and those of my Father and companions felt there was a faint hope for the dog.

Over the next few days and then weeks, we moved more and more frequently among the herds of cattle both on our own stance and to help our neighbours with their herds.

Dag remained calm and gradually I allowed him more and more freedom until the day came when I could send him round a herd, like a sheepdog, where he would firmly encourage them to move in the direction I indicated.

I whistled controls with my fingers and we established a very good working relationship and in three months I had a very confident and successful cattle dog, to my own surprise and that of family and friends.

But he still had a very vicious streak and this became apparent when a particularly rowdy crowd of drovers came to put their beasts in our stance and then use the accommodation barn. They were young, rude, aggressive Scotsmen and distressed my parents with their shouting and yelling.

I went to remonstrate and on entering the barn was immediately set upon by two men who had been drinking. I love a fight! But not against six men. These first two were the largest and I quickly realised I had to overcome them.

My elbow went into the nearest face with great force and I followed this up with a kick to the knee of the next antagonist. Both fell, attempted to rise and I waded in with boots and fists till they both lay on the ground, well beaten. I expected to be attacked from behind by the rest of the crew, but they cowered in a corner menaced by the most ferocious looking enormous animal imaginable.

It was my Dag.

I called him to my side, explained the rules of behaviour to these drovers and quietly left them to their labours repairing the damage to their companions.

What a find. My so-called useless dog had just shown what an intimidating presence he had. That killer instinct that I thought had gone was clearly evident in that small room. It would have to be very carefully controlled but in my work, extremely useful.

Drovers by their occupation are a rough, ready and very tough. You have to be able to live mostly outdoors with your cattle, ever watchful for thieves rustlers and robbers, certainly when returning home with a vast amount of money from the sales.

Only my experiences in the Highlands of Scotland kept me ahead in the local brawls but somebody at my back, like Dag would be a big advantage.

I determined to explore this part of his nature a lot more, to find out just how much control I could exert on this magnificent dog.

Steady work brought much needed money to both my Father and me, and coupled with other monies I had made all was going along smoothly.

Then reality set in. Father indicated he had received a letter from Solicitors acting for a man who wished to buy the House and Farm from him and named a very good price. As the only member of the family left at home, he said if I could match the offer in time he would wait but I could not expect to live on the farm forever unless I bought it from him; he had the other sons and daughters to think about and his own retirement.

He suggested I should now commit to being a drover in my own name, make my way in the world and stand on my own two feet.

With my savings and some smuggling money I had earned, there was enough, just, to buy a herd of cattle so my decision was made and acted on.

So with 'Good Luck' cries ringing in my ears I set off in the early summer on my way for the long walk from Brough under Stainmore, my home town, to the Dumfries Cattle Market in Scotland.

It was late July 1818 when I left and my intention was to walk the drovers' road from here to Dumfries calling in at resting houses, doss houses or sleeping rough as I had to conserve my money as much as possible to have enough to make the down payment on my first cattle.

A few years ago, whilst droving throughout England and Scotland for both my Father and others I came across a pack man, Reuben O'Connor and his irascible donkeys. Through him I became a part time smuggler of tobacco and tea and I've made enough money from that to have a large amount on my person.

Sovereigns are carefully sewn into my clothing making it very heavy but that's something I can live with. At all times I try to appear as a humble man looking for work but I'm tall and now well built and this does not always work for me.

Walking with a steady stride, my wolfhound at my side my intended route was to Appleby, Long Marton, Kirby Thore, Eamont Bridge near Penrith then Carlisle. I enquired about crossing the Solway Firth as a shortcut but was warned about the quicksands and dangerous tides, so I'd go to Gretna then Annan and be in Dumfries in eight days or less.

Heavy grey clouds gathered in the distance as I walked and Appleby came up by noon but I continued and walked on a lot further to Kirby Thore for a night's rest. Lodgings here are primitive, candles for light, straw mattress to sleep on but a pint of beer to slake my thirst. I paid for my beer and lodgings and settled into a dark corner Dag the wolfhound under my pew.

Watching quietly I studied the others in the room. Most were farm workers. There was one tramp, some packhorse men who I nodded to and four young men playing cards.

Vaguely at the back of my memory I recalled the landlord had a rather buxom and feisty daughter who I had playfully teased and joked with when I last visited. Perhaps I had promised to write or send a message to her once I left but as usual it went out of my mind and I did nothing. If she appeared I would have to profess no knowledge of this matter.

After a second pint of beer and a welcome home made pie, I stood and made for the door to leave for my room when the daughter appeared.

One look and I knew I had previously upset the lass.

"You horrid rascal, Jack Rutherford. I cried my eyes out for two whole weeks after you ran out on me."

Now that was not how I remembered it. Yes, I had taken a drink or two and I did blow her a kiss as I left but it was nothing of any moment, well not to me.

She created on and on, to make me feel small, but I just smiled and kept quiet. But two men rose from the table and as I thought went to persuade Molly to stop shouting and moaning. But it quickly became apparent that one of the men was 'sweet' on her and he felt an obligation to confront me, raising his voice and calling me a rascal.

I stood and waited. The second man came at me from my left side with a heavy swing at my chin. I ducked, kicked his knee out with a sharp pop and took a blow on my shoulder from the sweetheart. Red mists came, I parried his next blow and hit him under his chin very hard. He choked and gurgled and went down fast.

Dag stood next to me and the room went very quiet apart from the gagging and weeping from my two assailants. Molly was white, the card players stayed exactly as they were and the landlord remarked, "Don't come here again, Jack."

He gave me my accommodation money back, I gathered my kit and left to spend the night under the hedgerows. Of course it was raining heavily and I was fortunate to find and spend a rotten night in a leaky nearby barn, frozen cold and very hungry by morning time.

Feeling a little sore about the knuckles, Dag and I set

off walking again making for Eamont Bridge which we reached before noon and walked on to Penrith.

There, carefully choosing a quiet dwelling where we were unknown, we slept in a barn after a hearty dinner and begged some cold porridge for our breakfast.

Then off again on the road and its twenty miles from Penrith to Carlisle and it took all day to cover that distance and we eventually found accommodation in the Scotch Arms Hotel in Rickersgate at a reasonable price as the Drove Inn was full and we attempted to keep out of trouble as much as possible

Carlisle, Gretna, Annan all were passed through and we met many drovers, tinkers and pack horse men all heading for Dumfries and the massive market on Whitesands, the traditional site of the sales.

Joining the throng of people walking along to the market, we all nodded and spoke to each other, remarking on the changeable weather, stock prices, scoundrel tinkers, greedy landlords, in fact all the usual banter of men and ladies on the move to a big event.

When the sun came out, it was very hot and dusty with the constant flow of perspiring horses pulling heavy carts laden with colourful market goods. Pannier men walked at the head of their slowly plodding donkeys, each carrying pots, pans, pegs, household bits and pieces essential to the rural household. Soldiers marched alongside with a military step commanding a way through the throng on their way probably to a Garrison Town in Scotland where there was always unrest.

At last Dumfries, and when we arrived it was absolutely crawling with cattle, buyers, stockmen and drovers, men in tails and top hats, ladies in long sweeping dresses, market girls in headscarves and shawls that early August day in 1818 when I made my way over there.

I had taken cheap lodgings for the night, leaving my wolfhound Dag to fend for himself outside.

Talk on the road was that a lot of cattle were coming in from the Highlands of Scotland and good trade was expected. That could be in my favour or not, I was buying and my margin was extremely tight.

I had, by my calculations, just enough money to pay up to fifteen per cent down for my first real herd.

As I've said, it is the custom at these sales to agree a purchase price for the beast and then negotiate a minimum amount to be paid there and then in cash and a Letter of Credit is given for the balance and an agreed date for this to be paid.

Many unscrupulous drovers never reappear. They just vanish with any profits and so sellers are very wary of newcomers, reputation is everything and the risks taken by buyers and sellers are high.

Ten per cent is considered a good starting point for negotiation and haggling over both the price of the herd and the deposit can be a very vexed subject and the start of some intense rivalry, and I was a new face that day.

There was perhaps one thing in my favour. My Father had traded here for more than fifteen years and his reputation for honesty is second to none and this fact was the one I was relying on to strike a profitable bargain.

I was also looking round to employ drovers to help me on the long journey to York and these men need paying weekly, another thing to keep in mind. Employing men was a new experience for me but I had my Father's advice on this. I calculated that York Market is some one hundred and fifty miles approximately which at fifty miles per week would take me three weeks if all went well. It only needed floods and a closed bridge and my costs would run away very quickly.

From my lodgings next morning I rose from the sagging mattress and heard cattle lowing noisily in the background as I washed in icy cold water from the jug and basin, trimmed my hair and beard and brushed down the clothes I had been wearing all night. My room was very small and sparsely furnished with a rusty metal framed bedstead and a straw mattress covered in stained ticking. One threadbare blanket was provided so I slept fully clothed.

Downstairs I enjoyed some cold porridge for breakfast, saved some for my dog and after a reasonable night's sleep felt ready for the day.

Dressed in my working clothes of stout boots, leather gaiters, breeches, shirt and smock, I donned my hat and set off, in some excitement, to haggle with the hard men selling their black cattle.

At nearly 6' tall and broad shouldered, I stood above most of the crowd and was in a position to view all the beasts on display and move slowly through the throngs of buyers, sellers, onlookers and drovers. The sights and smells were very familiar to me from the many occasions I had accompanied my Father to these types of market, both here on Whitesands, Dumfries and at Falkirk Tryst.

It's necessary to slowly walk round all the many holding areas to view exactly what's on offer and gauge some idea of the condition of the beasts. They will have had a long walk down through Scotland and there was a lot more walking to be done. Lame animals were to be avoided as were those whose feet looked swollen or sweaty.

It was warm work but necessary and my wanderings and enquiries paid off when I spotted a herd of approximately two hundred cattle in a remote corner of the Mart. They were about one year old but woefully thin and the asking price reflected this. I moved into discussions with the farmer and had almost agreed a price when two men approached and attempted to shoulder me out of the way.

I reacted vigorously and Dag growled menacingly but they persisted and started negotiating with the vendor in a very abrupt and intimidating manner.

Now I had suggested £8.00 per head which was cheap and indicated ten per cent cash up front and my Letter of Credit. It turned out this man who was interrupting was known as Silas Kirk, a former soldier discharged for bad conduct after the Battle of Waterloo. I'd heard talk of this scoundrel who rarely kept his word and used strong arm tactics to get his way.

Kirk started talking £8.10s but no deposit. The seller

was clearly dismayed at this and turned to me for my offer but Kirk threatened me.

"Ease off now or I will take extreme measures and flatten you on the ground," were the words I chose to use, in some anger. This scoundrel bristled at my response and threatened me with a vigorous wave of his fists.

"You young whippersnapper," he said. "Be off with you before I beat you into pulp. You should take note of who you are talking to!"

So be it.

We had further strong words then and he became more and more angry at not getting his own way, until shouting and yelling, he swung a low punch to my side. I was hurt by the blow but then I saw red and hit him very quickly on the side of his head. He reacted with a punch to my stomach but I was ready and tensed every muscle as I saw the blow coming. It was then I recalled him being a soldier and more than capable of a good scrap, so I hit him very hard and deadened his shoulder and then kicked him between the legs. He buckled over squealing loudly and the nearby cattle became very nervous and frisky.

That seemed to settle things and he crawled away, weeping in agony.

His companion had taken no part in the scuffle as my dog was stood over him. They moved away cursing me and then Kirk quietly whispered, "You're a dead man."

After I caught my breath and settled the dog, I tracked the very nervous seller down and started negotiations once again.

It appeared he represented a number of small farmers in the Montrose region who had all fallen on hard times and funded this one man and four dogs to drove all the way to Dumfries for a sale. It was now late in the day, much of the cattle dealing was over but in talking and negotiating it seemed the price of £8.10s was acceptable but a cash deposit was absolutely vital to keep the farmers going until the sales had been completed.

By pure chance this particular farmer had met and dealt successfully with my Father four years previously so after a great deal of haggling we agreed £8.10s with a ten per cent cash up front, a total of £170 which I could just manage from my £300 savings. I drew up the Letter of Credit I had created and filled in the details which showed I had to bring £1,530 to this very market in exactly three months' time.

Sale completed I looked around and spotted three young men, late arrivals to the Mart and dressed in the traditional garb of drovers who could be looking for work.

I approached them and asked if they were interested in a drove to York. They demurred at York but would like to work for me so we talked things over and eventually agreed they would accompany me as far as Brough and I was relieved when they eagerly said yes to this proposal. This was a good start. They were all from a droving background but a little young to be starting on their own, about the age I first started in the trade.

A going rate is about £1.5s.0d. per week which they

accepted and I gave them ten shillings each to hold their promise, the rest at the end of each week.

Together we collected the herd and after Dag had carefully smelled and checked these new arrivals, we took the herd to the nearest halfpenny field and left my new men in charge to care for them overnight, taking shifts and sleeping rough.

Wandering back to my lodgings I carefully considered just what I had done and calculated that with care and good weather I could get this herd to York in about three weeks which I would discuss tomorrow with my workforce.

I went to seek some food as my stomach was rumbling in discontent. I had eaten very little since breakfast. And as I recalled the events at the Mart, if all the rumours were true, I had made a very bad enemy in Silas Kirk and his cutthroats. Cattle drovers are always using remote roads and wild places, thieving and robbing, even murder, are not unknown and the death threat may have been no idle matter. After meeting such a vicious and violent person at the Mart, I decided it might be a good idea to make some careful enquiries.

CHAPTER 4
SILAS KIRK

The Grapes Inn in Dumfries was a very old and well established premises much frequented by the drovers I knew and of course by a lot of other market traders, stall holders, tinkers and similar.

Walking into the bar I bought a small beer and as the landlord was taking a breather I raised the subject of Silas Kirk. Did he know him and could he tell me of his background. A long silence ensued and after a very careful look around to ensure nobody could overhear, he said, "I'd heard you had a run in with him and you have made a very bad enemy there. He's a former Army man with a reputation for violence and murder although nothing has ever been proven. His victims disappear leaving no trace."

I studied my beer, my curiosity roused.

"Tell you what though," he said, "over there in the corner is Jed Scurragh who although you wouldn't think it, fought with the 2nd Battalion the Coldstream Guards at Waterloo and knows something about that swine Kirk. Take him a pint of beer, sit down and ask him for some background."

This I did and walked over, introduced myself and asked if he had ever met my Father. He stated, "I've known your Dad George Rutherford for nigh on forty years, all of them good and I'm right glad to make your acquaintance, lad. What can I do for you? Rumour has it you've had a coming together with that sod Kirk and left him the worse for wear."

I brought him up to date with the situation and he was surprised I had still managed to buy the herd I had negotiated for.

He'd come across Kirk on the battlefield at Waterloo where he was a member of the Corps charged with disposing of battlefield dead by burial. British Army regulations, supposedly vigorously applied, meant that corpses on the field of battle are buried with as much dignity as possible, the grave being carefully marked for future reference with a cross and named and number.

Kirk's small platoon had gained a terrible reputation of stripping bodies of all valuables, removing rings, bracelets, money, notes in fact anything that could be converted into cash.

In reality the field of battle became a hunting ground for locals, vagrants, soldiers and camp followers who removed anything of value from the dead and sometimes not quite dead. It was alleged by Jed that wounded men had been knifed, stripped of belongings and hastily buried without any mark of respect or mark of their whereabouts. After so many such incidents were reported to the British Army, Kirk and some companions were investigated but little or no evidence could be found of their misdemeanours, only very strong rumours.

According to Jed, Kirk was booted out of the Army and turned loose into the Belgian countryside to fend for himself, having been stripped of all Army uniform. Strong rumours then came back that Kirk had gathered similar ruthless men and established a business of procuring young Belgian and French ladies to be sold for cash to the highest bidders in England. Big sums of money were involved and Kirk covered his tracks extremely carefully, using blackmail, extortion and murder where any person took a close interest in his affair.

So this was the man I was up against. I asked Jed if he had any weaknesses that I could exploit. He reckoned none. "Just remember he's a killer and very quick. Give him no quarter and watch your back."

Wise words. I thanked him and the landlord and left the tavern to put in some thinking.

CHAPTER 5
GISELLE DURRAND

Leaving the tavern I was in very deep thought at first and then realised that was exactly when I would be vulnerable to an assault.

Dumfries was still packed with horse traders, housewives at Market, young men showing off on horses, wagons rolling along and the streets all thronging with a multitude of people going about their business. Market days like this attract huge numbers of people who wish to sell local produce and buy goods from the packhorse men and traders who conduct a very steady trade.

All this I took in carefully and maintained my vigilance and this must have communicated to this damned great big wolfhound that I now owned. Dag was now my constant companion, brilliant with cattle, docile with people until roused when he became a very savage attack dog.

In the bright light of this August evening, shadows formed in the little alleys between the houses giving a strange darkness to areas that should have been brighter.

I saw these alleys as possible danger points and watched each entrance for signs of trouble. In one small alley I could hardly believe my eyes when I saw two men actually beating a young lady with a cane as I passed its narrow dark entrance near the market.

Quickly I moved across the throng of passers-by and stepped in to the alley to confront the villains.

With Dag at my feet we must have presented a formidable image. They unhanded the lady, threw her to the ground and turned to attack me.

It was unfair really. Dag had one man by the throat in seconds and I fought off the crazed blows of the main antagonist. He swung at me twice with his cane but I moved fractionally and avoided its blows then went in very hard, snapped his wrist and kicked him in the ribs as he lay writhing on the ground.

Blood was pouring from his companion's throat and I commanded Dag to leave go, which he did.

Both stared at me very hard and the main assailant said, "Do you not recognise who I am?"

I retorted, "A thug who attacks and injures young ladies, I suspect."

I then realised he was Silas Kirk and in the next breath he swore, again, that he would kill me very soon. A kick to his ribs stopped that conversation. I took the young lady by the hand, helped her to her feet and escorted her past the blood and gore and moved into the main street.

I hadn't really looked at her but she murmured her thanks in a broken English accent and at that point I looked and realised she was filthy dirty, dressed in rags but nevertheless a very attractive young lady. In fact she was gorgeous and it shone through despite her awful attire. My heart started a rapid thumping.

We walked quickly away from the scene and after some yards she stumbled and almost fell, but then I offered her my arm which she took.

It felt very natural and strangely exciting to be walking together linked in each other's arms and I asked her name. She replied, "Giselle," and from her speech I could tell she was French but with a command of English. She had been forcibly taken by Kirk and his men from her home in St Omer, France after they had killed her parents. She was destined to be wed to a rich man in Cumberland who had paid Kirk a large fee to capture her and bring her to England as a virgin.

I knew then that I had to give her protection and despite my very urgent need to be away from the immediate area of the market, I took her to a Mrs Nixon's private house that my Father had used for local accommodation. I explained what I intended to do, took her to the door and God Bless Mrs Nixon, she took pity and agreed to care for her, for a fee which I paid. We spoke together for over an hour.

Quietly I gave some of my money to Giselle and gave her my name and address in Brough, sincerely hoping she would want to see me again. She had quite turned my head and when she gave me a kiss on the cheek, I left with some great reluctance.

I was taken with her appearance and beauty and I went to my accommodation in a maelstrom of thoughts centred largely on a very attractive dark haired lady with an enquiring gaze and a delightful figure that I could just make out. This could be tricky.

It was an early start the next morning to collect my cattle and men, it was with fond memories of my encounter with that lovely lady that I embarked on a long and hazardous journey.

CHAPTER 6
LONG ROAD TO BROUGH AND REUBEN CONNOR

Cautious as always around cattle on the move, I had spotted in the distance one of probably Kirk's cutthroats watching our every movement. I assembled my drovers, collected my herd and set off from Dumfries on the road back south, making for Annan. Stops were made daily every ten miles to rest and feed the herd overnight in the halfpenny fields on the route and judging from their reaction, this was the very pasture the cattle were looking to enjoy and I was thankful for this as their condition left me nervous.

Always lurking not far away but not near enough to be attacked by Dag was one of Kirk's men, watching and waiting.

My drovers were young men of sixteen and seventeen and incapable of a hard fight with trained former soldiers so I warned them of the dangers and suggested they keep a good watch, particularly at night when the herd rested. This was the time when an attack would take place.

Long days on the road and the constant watchfulness

took its toll on me. Night duty meant walking round the sleeping animals and my sleep would have been negligible had not Dag taken over in the very small hours and accompanied one of the young men at all times. Fortunately it was late summer, the nights were warm and there was little rain in the first week and we made Annan in three days having rested one day.

Skirting the edge of the Solway Firth, we made our steady progress towards Gretna, sleeping rough and constantly on the alert for an attack which was sure to come.

Near Gretna the weather broke and heavy rain fell for hour after hour leaving us soaked to the skin, cold and with no prospect of a covered roof that night.

Dark overcast conditions later that night, no moon and a very open stance left me in no doubt that this would be the moment to attack us when the men were exhausted, tired, wet through and lacking any form of cover from the rain and wind.

So Dag and I left the crew with strict instructions to maintain a watch that changed every hour so the men had at least two hours sleep in three.

We went hunting. There is only one road to and from Annan to Gretna and we were on the stretch near Gretna so the likelihood was that the attackers would gather on the Annan side and creep forward to ambush us.

Together the dog and I crawled back the way we had come with our senses alert then hiding and it was Dag that sensed them first, as I hoped he would. There were three men moving stealthily down the road carrying cudgels and sticks whispering about the prospects of their reward. It seemed their intention was to knock us all unconscious, tie us up and steal my cattle receipt, hoping to move quickly to Carlisle, sell the cattle before we could give chase and take the cash to Kirk. All this as they passed by in the dark.

Really it was far too easy. They moved in single file and when not talking spread out about ten yards apart. I removed my boots, crept up to the rearmost man and coshed him hard, supported him as he fell and left Dag on guard. Moving swiftly in stocking feet, I caught the next man in exactly the same way and left him unconscious on the road. Just as I reached the leader he turned with some premonition and this time I hit straight to his throat. He gagged and fell where I laid him unconscious with a further blow to the head.

Three down, not bad. I crept slowly back, collected and put on my boots and joined Dag. We tied each man up before he came round and when they were capable of standing, pushed them ahead of us back to the herd. I whistled once to announce our arrival and was glad to see all three men wide awake with stout sticks ready to defend our cattle.

With the thieves gagged and tied, we took turns sleeping and watching until dawn came and with it the incessant rain and an increasing wind. Our herd were restless with the rising gale and it was essential to get them quickly on the road to Gretna but what to do with the captives?

Well, sauce for the goose, sauce for the gander, I left them tied up in the field. They could be there yet for all I know.

Carlisle brought the prospect of a day's rest and the chance to meet up with that bastard Reuben Connor, packhorse man, smuggler and villain. My kind of man but on my terms.

I originally met this wily old packhorse man some months earlier by chance in a tavern near Carlisle. He sat in the corner of the room almost out of sight and I only became aware of him as I sat down with my beer. Slowly we talked, exchanged names and livelihoods. My Father was on a short drove in the area and he was at the bar in another room talking to friends.

Reuben owned six donkeys and trod the length of the North from Falkirk in Scotland to the great port of Liverpool. Up and down the area he bought and sold anything to make a profit. Iron goods and tools from blacksmiths, corn, linen, pegs for washing lines, brushes and besoms, shirts, clothing, anything that women and men in remote parts of the countryside could afford to buy.

Grizzled, worn, cantankerous and cunning, I knew of him by reputation. He was well built but a little bent with age when he went to the bar, filled his tankard with a mild beer and brought me a fill for my pot. We talked pleasantly for a long while until two men appeared and bought ale. They had a furtive look about them both and Dag growled deeply under the bench we sat on.

Reuben became quiet and looked very nervous. He

came to leave and no sooner was he out of sight, having wished me a good night, than the newcomers rose and followed him out, one drawing a knife as he closed the door.

Dag and I moved quickly out into the street to see Reuben down on the ground being kicked by one man while the other brandished his knife. I moved in rapidly and felled the knifeman with a very hard blow to the back of his neck. Dag had the other man by the throat slowly chocking him to death.

At my whispered command, Dag drew off on guard and I saw a knife sticking out of Reuben Connor's arm. I quickly removed it, and pierced the hand of his assailant with the blade into a nearby door post. That slowed him down a lot and the dog's presence added to his remaining very still.

Reuben had lost some blood but had defended himself from this sudden attack as only a hardened packhorse man could, but two against one had been difficult odds to manage.

My intervention had saved his life; hot water and bandages in the tavern helped me to see to his injury and we discussed what to do with his assailants. Our remote location in the city meant there was no jail to hand them in and my suggestion to let Dag kill them was frowned on.

After some long thought we tied them up to a nearby tree and left them to it, but not before I broke the right wrist of each of them. No more knife work for a while for them.

As it turned out, in nervous conversation Reuben let slip that he was also a smuggler and these men were after his contraband, in this case whisky and tobacco. In our conversation whilst he slowly recovered over a beer he left me with the distinct impression that should I need anything at all, he would provide it. Anything.

He was grateful, in his miserly way, that I had saved his life.

So some months later, there I was, waiting in darkness outside a very remote tavern to collect some tobacco and tea from the scoundrel. His idea of a good price is one where he gains maximum benefit. We'd had strong words and a decent arrangement for cash had been agreed. But I wouldn't trust him and despite his professed duty to me I was highly suspicious.

But I needed cash to buy my first herd of cattle and I was £78 short of my total. With great care I had sounded out all the local landlords in the area as I travelled and found a ready interest in tobacco and strangely enough tea. On careful enquiry it seemed the gentry in the area would be delighted to have 'a little tea' for their social gatherings, if the price was right.

Reuben had suggested I could contact him by word of mouth with any passing pack horse man or tinker which I had done two months before suggesting we meet for 'goods' at this remote tavern near Tebay.

I knew he was nearby as I had scouted round and found his six donkeys hidden in a field so it looked promising.

Entering the tavern, I left Dag outside and ordered a small beer which I took over to Reuben's table. He greeted me carefully and watchfully. Yes, he had the goods and named a stupid price. I looked at him long and hard and as I stood to leave, he touched my hand and asked me to stay.

We bargained very hard and he was very angry at the final sum, but in the end I bought all I needed for £24 which was all I had available on me.

We left together but he asked me to wait while he brought the goods to me. When he reappeared I used his lantern to double check just what I had bought and sure enough the 'tea' leaves were from a nearby bush.

Dag held him to the ground while I took the lantern, found his donkeys and identified the tea leaves by their distinctive smell. I took them and left him his rubbish.

Strangely he hadn't moved much. Dag stood back and I discussed Reuben's parentage at length, his foul way of treating a friend and gave him a kick up the arse as he left, muttering nastily.

My way home took me down the Eden Valley which was the only route I could take and I noticed some cattle nearby and spoke to the farmer who appeared at his gate.

They were thin beasts and would take some careful management but it could just be done once I had them home in Brough. They were very desperate to sell and needed the money to survive. There was the husband, a wife and two small children, all in rags and waiting to face a grim winter. Standing talking and giving it some thought, though I was then penniless I had some money saved at home and knew my Letter of Credit was now acceptable as cash so I negotiated a reasonable price at the farm gate, told them to buy goods for themselves on my Credit note and would collect the beast in the next three weeks' time.

That conversation with the farmer, the offer of a night's rest and food delayed my arrival in the next town, Kirby Stephen effectively three days after I had negotiated with Reuben. Going into the town I hid my spoils in the corner of a quiet field and wandered into the nearest tavern to slake my considerable thirst. That small beer tasted just fine and I savoured the taste as I sat down at last.

No sooner was I on the bench resting that two Revenue Men charged in and tried to pounce on me. Little good did it do them. I beat them off quickly and when they were a little more willing to have a normal conversation I found they had evidence I was in possession of illicit goods.

After a heated discussion we went through all my clothing, harness and tackle and found nothing. They appeared somewhat crestfallen and apologised brusquely.

That bastard Reuben had shopped me but my instincts had proved correct. Leaving the goods where they were for the moment I made to leave for home but I resolved to return only when I had a careful check of the area and some firm buyers for my goods.

Three weeks later I returned for the cattle I had bought and took a food parcel to the farmer as a quiet gift.

He was in tears, as was his wife and they gave me a

nice send off by walking some of the way with the cattle which helped me enormously as there was only me and Dag.

I timed my return through Kirby Stephen to be in darkness, having placed the cattle in a stance on the outskirts. After a very careful check of the area, Dag and I crept into the field and recovered all my contraband.

Back at the stance I placed it under two beasts with a bag suspended under their bellies and in this way, next day, we cleared the town and within the morning had these cattle on good fresh pasture that we owned.

So that's the rotten villain I was about to meet in Carlisle and thankfully our negotiations concluded very swiftly, mostly in my favour as Reuben was anxious to move on. Tea was my main purchase this time and was again hidden under the bellies of my cows and out of sight.

After leaving Carlisle, it was the long hard slog of twenty one miles to Penrith which took the best part of three days then the familiar road through the Eden Valley to Brough, another twenty five miles and home.

CHAPTER 7
STAINMORE TO BOWES

Giselle's gentle shake brought me out of my stupor.

"Where am I?" was my first reaction on coming round, then the cruel pain in my leg and the enormity of our situation hit me. I was devastated.

She left me briefly and with Dag's help caught the horse used by one of the villains and brought it over to me. With extreme difficulty I managed to catch the horse's bridle and pull myself erect.

Over some reassuring words and gentle encouragement, the horse was led to the corpse, with me walking alongside and, with Giselle's help and despite the pain, I loaded one onto the horse's back. We then went to the edge of the bog where I left him. I went back, again, for the other body and laid them out.

Together we rolled the corpses into the morass and watched as they slowly sank below the surface until all that remained were bubble and the foul stench of fetid water.

My hope was that the bog would swallow them without trace and I left all their belongings and clothing on them.

Their form of dress was too distinctive by far and despite them having very little money I took what they had and I was greatly relieved at their disappearance.

That horse too was known locally and could not be taken very far but we mounted together and I rode as far as I dared towards the herd before I sent him back to his stable with a smart smack on his rump and a growl from Dag.

Then we started the long walk to catch up with my herd. It was eight miles to Bowes by my calculations and, fit as I was, there was a long hard slog across that bleak landscape with no hope of any rest.

Duncan and my hands knew that the cattle had to be kept on the move to reach Bowes before nightfall. Dragging my wounded knee, we spent the next hour staggering forward through the rough path, each step an agony and it was only cold anger at my fate and a fierce determination to reach the herd that kept me going. Despite the cold of higher ground, I was sweating profusely and all our water was with the packhorse and the herd of cattle. Onward we trod with Giselle giving me her shoulder to brace on and ease my walking and in this way we caught up with the herd and the precious water I so desperately needed.

At my shouted command, the herd was stopped by passing word down the line to Duncan at the front of the drive.

We gathered round and I explained in small detail the confrontation that had taken place indicating that the two men were last seen walking away across a very desolate and notoriously treacherous stretch of moorland. Giselle said nothing.

Once we had set off, slowly, very slowly, Bowes appeared in the distance down in the valley. We had taken a high road across the moor to be able to watch for thieves and robbers who would willingly steal a cow.

Now we commenced the steady drop and I was relieved beyond words to finally see the cattle in their overnight stance and the Unicorn Hotel beckon with its candle lit windows. We managed to find rough quarters in an outbuilding. Duncan Foster and I agreed with my companions a night watch rota.

All this time Giselle had watched me grimacing with pain and at last I agreed to have my leg attended to. She had begged some fresh linen from the hotel and found some sort of salve in her belongings. This she applied to my wound and bandaged me again. Our evening meal was a pie with meat provided, at a cost, by the hotel and we wolfed it down then settled on the floor for a broken night's sleep.

What I did like was that, after her evening ablutions, Giselle settled by my side gave me an encouraging kiss and went quietly to sleep holding my hand.

CHAPTER 8
BOWES TO
SCOTCH CORNER

Morning found us awake to an early start and after some coarse bread and a small beer we were about to set off again with our herd of restless cattle, making for Scotch Corner. I had no option but to negotiate for a very tired looking horse that the landlord just happened to have for sale. Money, as always, was tight but Giselle hit on the notion of selling him one of the cattle in the herd. His meat pies were well known far and wide for their quality. Not only did we receive the horse but she managed to include a supply of pies to see us along our way and this proved the making of our next few days journey.

Together as much as possible, Giselle and I fell to easy conversation about the drove, the prospects of success and of course, my ambitions, and in all this she displayed a wonderful desire for knowledge, not just about the drove and the cattle but about me and my plans. Very subtle that girl.

Mounted on the horse, over the course of the route my leg improved, our food supply lasted longer than anticipated and we made the twenty seven miles to Thirsk in Yorkshire five days later, having stopped to rest the herd for a day on the route.

York is some twenty odd miles from Thirsk and we set off in good time for the steady trek to Market. It would be three days' steady walking through flat pleasant country mostly down to wheat and oats from my view on the road. Surprisingly the horse we negotiated for in Bowes picked up condition nicely with good pasture along the way and some decent care and attention from Giselle.

Riding in to Thirsk, Giselle and I made some enquiries from passers-by and heard talk that a ready buyer for some of the animals could be found with the local butcher.

We found him eventually and he was willing to buy four sturdy beast at a good price, the money came in very useful later on.

Near Coxwold we had a near disaster when we tried desperately to stop the herd to allow a coach and four to pass quickly and noisily by. The herd hate these contraptions and experience taught us to try to spot them from afar by the dust cloud and gather the herd together and calm them as the carriage went past. Not this time, slight damp had reduced the dust and the coach was upon us very quickly.

That Coxwold stop was dreaded as the herd was panicked by the carriage and four and started to career down the lane away from the noise and headed straight for a distant gate to a field of young wheat just showing good growth.

An absolute disaster was averted by the very quick reactions of a young man who ran pell mell to the gate, closed it and joined Dag at the front of the herd to slow them to a walk again, A very close call! We caught up as quickly as we could and thanked him for his prompt action while Duncan cursed the coach driver and waved his fists as the vehicle disappeared in the distance.

This stranger whose name was George Cook asked if he could help move the beasts as he was of farming stock and making, like us, for York and the Market.

I agreed a rate of pay on a daily basis with him and he quickly settled in to our routine and showed a great interest not only in our herd but had an ability with animals that was uncanny. Always calm and quiet, he cleverly anticipated every trick that those wild young cattle might attempt and he thwarted them each time.

CHAPTER 9
GEORGE COOK
AND YORK SALES

George Cook, it turned out, was a wonderful and experienced man and rarely did anything upset him. He got on well with everybody, Giselle, Duncan – my Topman, and all the new young drovers who came and went as we moved down country.

That first evening when we had settled the herd and found rough accommodation we talked at length. He was from Bilsdale, a valley to the North in the Cleveland Hills and was a drover by trade but had been unable to find work on the farms in his area.

He had recently delivered a small herd of fifty cattle from York to Newcastle and was now back with his four dogs hoping to find further work in York. Like me, he stood tall and looked lean and fit with a no nonsense look about him and I must admit we got along very well from the start.

Over the next few days, as we came nearer to York we all came to appreciate his fine qualities as both a professional drover and as an honest trustworthy man.

Twice I left money in his sight but not a penny was touched and when Giselle lost some small coin it was George that found it and returned it.

Giselle was growing more and more in my estimation too. She acted carefully in my best interests and had a keen business sense and an ability to get things done without fuss. What worried me was a remark she quietly made in my ear, "*I will guide you in to getting your own way.*"

York was upon us, our cattle were settled for the night, watch keepers were appointed and once I had done my share of duty I looked forward to talking to Giselle, George and Duncan over a small beer and some food.

Morning saw us walking past the magnificent York Minster to the ground where the sales would take place. Cattle Markets are always busily alive with people going about their business, talking, pointing, gesticulating with hands or using hats, sticks and sometimes kerchiefs to attract attention.

George, Giselle, Duncan and I stood by our cattle to receive offers and negotiate any sales that day. Local farmers viewed the beasts knowing full well they were either good for the table or would over winter and fatten for the spring sales and a good profit. I needed £10.5s at least to show a profit and pay my debts and over the course of the next two hours we managed to sell all our herd at a little over that figure. With one hundred and ninety nine cattle sold at roughly £10.5s each, I had in my possession some £ 2,089.0.0 which was a healthy sum to be carrying about. I was about to visit a local Solicitor I had been recommended to who would be willing to place my money in his safe. But I had to get there and any amount of low life had watched me collect an awful lot of money and I needed protection with coin and notes sticking out of every pocket. I was totally unprepared for the amount of money involved and the means to carry it, and George, Duncan and Giselle appeared to have left me, only Dag remained at my side.

Moving carefully through the crowd I realised I had to traverse a narrow alley to access the Minster area where the Solicitors' Office stood. Two surly youths stood across the alley entrance blocking my way. Dag showed a great keenness to be allowed to mingle competitively with these youths and they wisely fled just as George, Duncan and Giselle reappeared. The girl had needed the toilet and they had stood guard in the tavern.

Of the money I now had in my possession I owed £1530.00 on my Letters of Credit to be paid very shortly. My profit was £495.10 shillings.

I was about to leave the market as it was ready to close when some very sorry beasts came in to the mart. All the buyers had gone. The owner, a fat farmer looked around in disgust, threw his hands in the air and would have danced on his hat if he had remembered to wear it. He spotted me smiling and strode over full of hell. "What do you find so funny young man," he demanded.

I recalled my mission to bank my cash and made to leave when he stopped me and apologised for his behaviour.

He was a rich farmer arrived late at the mart through road delays and had one hundred and fifty thin miserable cattle to dispose of.

George Cook had watched the proceedings and took me to one side for a quick talk. George reckoned these animals could be bought cheap and taken south to Norfolk or Suffolk to be fattened through winter and sold in Smithfield Market in London in the spring time at a good healthy profit. We talked it over and I asked Giselle's advice as well. There was a huge risk with both a new friend, weak cattle and a long dangerous journey.

It was indeed a very big gamble and if I decided it was worth the risk it would depend on the terms of my Letter of Credit, the deposit needed and the repayment date.

I asked the farmer to give me few minutes and conferred with both George and Giselle. More and more I was able to include her in my planning and we were becoming very close to each other.

Finally after a lot of head scratching and calculation we reckoned if they could be bought below £8.0.0 and less than £105 down it could just be managed.

As George said, on the way south he could sell the occasional beast to cover his expenses and with only four dogs his costs were very low. Could it be done, that few dogs, one man and 150 cattle to control? George said that before each major town he could hire two men to see him through the area and pay them from sales to butchers on the way.

Our farmer was getting very agitated again but I told him to wait a few more moments for our decision. We would go for it!

Negotiations commenced and it soon became apparent that the animals were surplus to his needs and would cost a lot to feed over winter. We bartered and haggled but in the end we agreed a price of £7.12.6d each and my Letter of Credit for 4th April 1819 for £1057.3s. the deposit being eight per cent I paid him £ 86.0s.0d. and took a note of his name and address.

CHAPTER 10
SOLICITOR'S OFFER
GEORGE COOK GOES SOUTH

Promptly we repaired to the Solicitors' office near the Minster and after being asked to wait for a time we were ushered into the presence of Mr Aubrey Percival who seemed remarkably red faced and flustered in our presence.

Dressed in brown-waisted trousers with a green waistcoat and brown long jacket he personified the legal profession in all its expensive glory, but this was not the man who then spoke; he appeared extremely flustered and was florid about the face. He regretted keeping us waiting but had received startling news and was overcome with anxiety and begged our forgiveness.

We spoke at length and I agreed to leave the balance of my money, some £2002.0.0 in his safe overnight and at this point he took a lot more interest in me. That amount of money on a person of my age was very unusual. He asked if we could stay for a cup of tea and called his clerk over to make four cups with, he suggested, the very best china.

Great interest was then shown in my business affairs, how I had so much money, what was my background and who were my companions. Reluctantly I introduced Giselle and George Cook, listened to him and then I questioned his interest in my affairs. Slowly it emerged that he had the opportunity to purchase an option on a large acreage of land on the riverside in Stockton-on-Tees, but the only coach going there was smashed on the outskirts of York and his money for the purchase of the Option had to be in a Solicitors' office in Stockton by 8am the next day. Aubrey, for we were on first name terms by then, asked if I would be willing, for a fee, to take his cash and mine by horseback to Stockton, pay his Option fee and then continue to Brough and beyond.

Thoughts ran through my head and I mentally reviewed events to help me clarify what to do next.

George Cook was committed to taking one hundred and fifty cattle down to Suffolk to over winter to fatten then sell them in the spring at Smithfield Market. I had no spare cash to offer him.

Meanwhile Giselle had no home and it would be very important for her to be back at Brough which she knew only vaguely and to be introduced properly to my parents with a letter explaining that I planned to ask her to marry me as I had fallen madly in love with Giselle.

Now this offer from Aubrey Percival. I could let George take the cattle and sell beast along the way to cover his costs and feed expenses. It would be a huge gamble but just possible with a mild back end weather wise and the rich grasslands of Suffolk. Was George Cook a man I could rely on? Practically on his own with just his four dogs?

Next, and most important, Giselle. I loved her with all my heart and she had been a real stalwart on the journey down and we had grown more and more fond with each passing day. It all started when I just held her hand as we walked and talked and now I realised just how much we'd enjoyed each other's company and how I both relied on her judgement and realised I was deeply in love. But what about Giselle? She had followed me to Brough and undertaken this long journey but was she as smitten as I was?

My idea was to send a message via the coaches that I knew stopped in Brough and prepare my parents and ask them to make her welcome until my return.

Could I get to Stockton from York in the time suggested? With only two horses? I knew Dag would just follow where I went but it was a huge risk and I would be carrying not only my own money but Aubrey's as well. Highwaymen seem to know these things and Silas Kirk was still out there waiting to pounce.

Giselle and George waited while I let my thoughts clarify and then I made my decisions. Yes, I would take the money to Stockton but insisted on a substantial fee which was agreed and paid promptly in more cash.

Regarding the Sufffolk cattle, I gave George my suggestions and after a lot of thought he agreed and would start the next morning. He had some connections in that area which could stand him in good stead.

Then Giselle. I asked Aubrey if he had a private room I could use for a few moments and I asked a very puzzled young lady to join me. When I had quietly closed the door behind us, heart in my dry mouth, I took the biggest gamble of my life!

I went down on one knee and asked Giselle to marry me.

Bless my soul, she said nothing, just stared at me. It lasted a lifetime then she burst into tears and fell into my arms saying, "Yes, yes, please." We held each other tight for a long time and whispered endearments in each other's ears. We finally went back into the room holding hands and I announced that I had asked for Giselle's hand in marriage and she had agreed. There were whoops of joy from George and Aubrey and I was roundly congratulated while Giselle was kissed and then we returned to reality.

Letters were prepared for my parents which George and Duncan agreed would go by First Class Mail and Duncan would escort Giselle back to Brough via the slower standard coach giving time for matters to resolve properly, at least that's what I hoped.

For me, it was a fast trip back to Stockton-on-Tees.

CHAPTER 11
RACE TO STOCKTON

Hiring two horses was accomplished with some great difficulty at that time of night and it was after 10pm by the clock in the office before I could make my departure.

York to Stockton is sixty miles and in these summer conditions ten hours would be very good going.

My intention was to ride very hard overnight to arrive in Stockton before the 8am deadline which Aubrey, the Solicitor, had stressed was absolutely vital and this was going to be a very tight run affair.

But heavy rain was falling as I mounted the first horse outside the office near York Minster and set off through Bootham Gate, due north on the major road.

With Dag loping easily beside the second horse which was secured on a long halter, we cantered onward, knowing the roads would rapidly deteriorate to a complete muddy morass if this rain continued.

Rain soaked, we continued through the small villages, rarely pausing and making reasonable progress. Sutton on the Forest and Crayke were deserted that dark wet night but I had a knowledge of the route and despite having no lantern or candle, I could make out the correct road and continued.

Coxwold was the next village to head for as it was my intention to go through to Thirsk and then take the major carriage road from there to Northallerton and then through Welbury and Picton making for Kirklevington and Yarm.

Dawn was breaking at 6.30am by my rough reckoning and with the improving light I needed to stop again and change to the rested horse.

I was thoroughly soaked now and saddle weary, having ridden for over eight hours and I stopped under trees to shelter briefly and change to my fresh horse.

Remounted on the refreshed animal, my instincts told me I had about ninety minutes to reach the Solicitors' office in Finkle Street, Stockton, a place I was not familiar with but by then there should be people about to ask directions of.

Moving through the heavy mud, I became concerned for my progress and was heartily glad to reach the outskirts of Yarm and ride though the wide paved thoroughfare even though it was covered in about two inches of flood water.

My thoughts centred on the bridge over the River Tees being open and passable as it was known to flood in the area and close the major river crossing.

Reaching the bridge I noted three rough men demanding money to cross over and this combined with the swirling water around the structure made it look doubtful I could proceed further. I was furious at being so near to my objective and yet prevented from crossing this precarious bridge.

Turning quickly aside I moved into a nearby street to watch just what was happening and it became clear after a while that this was a local attempt at highway robbery using the pretext of the bridge's safety to demand a safe crossing sum. After all the effort and pain of carrying a huge amount of money with me, I had no intention of being stopped on that bridge. Three men could easily overwhelm me despite having my dog eager to do battle.

Quietly gathering my very tired tethered horse, I loosened its halter then turned onto the street, trotted fifty yards away from the bridge and then turned and spurred my horses and the dog at the bridge and galloped at full speed straight at them.

The men stood their ground for what seemed to me a long time but they dived out of the horse's path. Dag and I on my fresh horse ran straight over the bridge but I had released the tired horse just before we reached these men and sure enough it stopped quickly in the middle of the bridge completely exhausted. This stopped them from making any movement to hinder me.

Once over the bridge we slowed to a steady canter and made through to Stockton High Street and from there we were directed to Finkle Street and the office of Dyson W. Frobisher.

According to the clock in his office waiting room it was five minutes to eight and I demanded to see Mr

Frobisher immediately, but the whiskered elderly clerk muttered something about very busy and must have an appointment.

Storming across the room, I flung open the door in extreme anger to see a distinguished figure calmly sat at a huge desk who stated, "You seem to be in a hurry young man. Have you urgent business here?"

Holding my saddlebags in each hand, dripping with rain and very bedraggled, I might have seemed a little out of the ordinary, I must admit, but at the mention in a gasp of Aubrey Percival's name and my mission, understanding dawned on his face. He bade me sit down and quickly wrote down the precise time of my arrival.

Offering me a cup of tea greatly improved my demeanour and we entered into discussions.

CHAPTER 12
STOCKTON
SOLICITOR'S OFFICE

Aubrey Percival was purchasing some four hundred feet of River Tees frontage with the intention of developing it as a commercial wharf for the sailing ships that regularly came up river. The amount I brought was to be a deposit and the full purchase price was to be paid at a time to be specified in the future, perhaps next year.

Which set me thinking. I spoke at length to Mr Frobisher on the prospects for a wharf and frontage in Stockton and he agreed that Aubrey Percival, who he knew well and admired, was known to be a shrewd investor and likely to make a lot of money as the port developed.

Thinking things through, the Battle of Waterloo had defeated Napoleon and England was no longer at war, which would mean a reduction in the number of cattle to be sent for slaughter over the coming years. This was a moment when I had both the profits from my drive and the considerable fee from Aubrey Percival and even after I had paid all my debts in Scotland I had a little surplus.

So without further ado I asked Mr Frobisher if I could be included in the investment.

We discussed this for some time and he made it very clear to me that there would be a firm demand for the balance of the purchase price at a date to be established in the future, perhaps in a year.

Reaching into my saddlebags, I gave him Aubrey Percival's money and my own deposit which was £100 being five per cent of the £2000 I had agreed to pay. Once he had prepared my formal receipt, he sealed it in an envelope and gave it to my safe keeping having assured me he would write immediately to Mr Percival sending his receipt.

Here again another wild gamble and this time without any consultation with my future wife. Could be some strong words ahead.

Dyson Frobisher and I parted on very good terms. I liked the man and felt I could trust him although he made no mention of a personal involvement in this investment.

Weary now beyond words, I left Stockton making for Brough and a few miles on my journey found a drovers' resting place. Dag was fed, the horse was groomed and put in a stable with water and hay, and I had a meal and fell fast asleep in the roughest bed I have seen for some time. But I was dry and warm, so were my animals so I didn't worry.

CHAPTER 13
ATTEMPTED ROBBERY BY KIRK'S MEN

Leaving the outskirts of Stockton next day, feeling much refreshed, we made a steady progress north west to cover the almost fifty miles to Brough where I would rest before making for Dumfries again and meeting my Letters of Credit.

Four days' travel saw me in Brough to be greeted by Giselle who had arrived safely two days earlier with Duncan who confirmed the hired hands had cheerfully set out to walk back here. My Mother and Father had welcomed Giselle with open arms apparently delighted that I showed signs of settling down. Of course Giselle wanted a full description of my wanderings, but not half as much as she wanted to know about my investment and I had a hard time convincing her of the merit of my riverside venture.

It took some while as she is very commercially aware, I now realised, but eventually we believed it was a sensible involvement in a growing town.

To my intense delight both Mum and Dad found

Giselle wonderful company and I noticed her and Mother conferring a lot, not just on domestic matters but edging in to commercial matters too.

Two days after arriving home I set off again. Mounted on my horse and with Dag following, we commenced the journey to Dumfries but I would have to go through Carlisle where I would stop and hope to catch up with Reuben Connor.

I'd let it be known to passing packhorse men that I would like to meet up again and I was sure the message would be passed along the line in the usual way.

Still carrying a lot of money I was as alert as usual and it was in the remote area of high ground between Penrith and Carlisle that I first became suspicious we were being followed.

High Hesketh was the area the thieves chose to move in on me and again it was two men I eventually spotted who quite clearly felt able to expose their movements to give added anxiety to me. All the hallmarks of Kirk's villains, hired ex-soldiers confident in their abilities to rob and if necessary kill.

On my person I had my heavy stave, the dagger that I removed from my wolfhound's foot and a pistol. I'd bought this from a contact of Reuben's but kept it quiet from Giselle and my family.

So how would we play this out? They must know of Dag's capabilities now and were probably armed with a musket and that could prove to be the decisive weapon.

There was an option to stand and let them come to me but that meant they dictated the warfare.

Early October, the nights draw in and it's dark by about 7pm and I'm much more a hunter in the night as is Dag, so with that in mind I delayed my movements to identify a good ambush spot and once found, I made my small camp under a bush and appeared to settle down for the night.

After a suitable wait I bundled my coat into the appearance of a sleeping form and used a dark horseblanket under the saddle support to look like my dog.

We crept very quietly along the hedgeback on our bellies then out into the long grass in the nearby field and waited.

Two long hours passed with my eyes getting more and more heavy when my dog touched me with his paw and stared ahead into the gloom. With no moonlight it was just possible to make out shapes crawling, as we had done, towards our resting place where the horse snuffled to himself.

Five long minutes later there was a bang as they took a shot at what they assumed was my sleeping form. Murder attempt again, not good, but that musket took a minute to reload so we moved in quickly and Dag had one man pinned down by his throat I presumed and I left him in charge there.

Blood curdling sounds came from the area and the remaining villain stood to kill my dog.

My pistol blasted very close to him and he fell instantly and as I had resolved to question him, I deliberately wounded him in the thigh. He made a lot of unnecessary noise, howling with pain just as he probably expected me to do. Anyway I acquired a musket!

"Who sent you? How much were you paid?" Those questions left the man in no doubt that I was on to him.

"Silas Kirk gave me and him £20 to kill you and that dog of yours and I wish I'd succeeded after what you've done to my leg. He is scared stiff you will come after him and kill him and he intends to do that to you first."

Further questioning revealed that Kirk was growing very anxious that each of the men sent to 'deal' with me had disappeared without trace.

I left the two wounded men tied up by the roadside after questioning although they seemed loath for me to leave, but as I explained, with a kick, "You took your chance and it failed badly."

Packing my meagre belongings, I then found their belongings and was about to set off to leave the area when Dag went on alert and I heard the sound of many hooves.

Just when I didn't need anybody knowing what I had been up to. And if it was an Army patrol, well it didn't bear thinking about.

But the noise seemed vaguely familiar, so the dog, horse and I waited very quietly by the lane, hidden under bushes, when a packhorse man with six donkeys passed our temporary hideaway.

My quiet, "Good morning," made the packman jump almost out of his skin but he stopped and we talked at some length. He was curious to know what I was doing at that time of the morning and me, I had the same question for him.

Giving him a little baccy for his pipe, we spoke and it seemed he, like me, knew Reuben Connor. Indeed he became extremely nervous when I mentioned that name and with a little gentle enquiry it appeared he was on the run from Reuben.

Arthur, for that was his name, did a little smuggling but owed Reuben Connor a large sum which he was about to pay from some gold he had earned and a cache of money hidden on the Scottish Borders.

Distressed beyond measure that I may disclose his whereabouts, he explained that he had been robbed by two former soldiers of some of the gold and even with his cache could not meet his debt to Connor and that meant a very painful experience when they inevitably met again.

This coincidence could be used to my extreme advantage. I explained I had just had a meeting with the soldiers and seriously injured them and showed Arthur the huge hole in the back of my jacket that the musket shot had made.

So we searched afresh in the improving light and found some small belongings left behind when they went to kill me that included his gold and some other remains and ammunition for the musket.

Arthur's face was a picture of happiness in that early morning light and on the deserted road he gave a little jump of joy. I allowed his enthusiasm to express itself and then dampened his spirits with my next suggestion.

Arthur's donkeys were not carrying any load, his route back to Scotland would take him over some wild remote moorland, so why not pop these two murderers on the donkey's back, cover them with a sheet and drop them off in a remote part of the inhospitable moors and off the beaten track? I had no compunction in leaving the villains to their fate, such is the hard life I had chosen and it was each man for himself. There was a remote chance the injured men would survive but it was indeed very remote.

For this favour to me, I would not mention his whereabouts to Connor, and he could keep his gold and the musket and the ammunition.

It took a while to convince him but in the end he agreed. We loaded his donkeys and he set off for northern parts while I renewed my journey to Carlisle.

Once there, my enquiries of the packmen placed Reuben within two days of the city so I waited, met him, agreed to buy tobacco and tea which he would leave in an agreed hiding place and paid him up front but with the severe warning of what would befall him if he reneged on our deal.

Back to my horse, saddlebags and money secure under my rump, we traversed the long route to Dumfries and once there I placed an advertisement in the paper announcing my arrival where I would meet persons with my Letters of Credit and conduct such business as was considered seemly.

Making my presence known in this way ensured those I was in debt to would be aware of my intentions, but so would my enemies.

In the Grapes Inn, I asked Jed Scurragh if he could provide some burly muscle to afford me protection whilst I concluded my money matters and that was just what we did.

Three days after arriving I settled in to the bar of the Grapes, met the Montrose farmer and his colleagues and concluded our business after I showed them my book of accounts and detailed every penny gained and spent.

There was comment from the Montrose men on the profit I had shown but once I explained the distances involved, the weather conditions, thieves, vagabonds and scoundrels I had attracted, they left muttering but reasonably happy.

Then the return to Brough, Giselle and my family.

CHAPTER 14
MARRIAGE TO GISELLE

Carlisle was bustling as usual when I entered the city travelling home, and after stabling my horse after its food and water, I left Dag to fend for himself and took cheap accommodation to have a good rest and have an early start.

Back on the road next morning I cautiously approached the agreed hiding place for my tobacco and tea, found it to be intact, surprise, surprise, and then trod a long path back to Brough.

Ahead of me lay the joyful prospect of marriage to my Giselle but I could not help but worry that Kirk would have spies out and about and Giselle was very vulnerable to being held hostage. None of this had I mentioned at home but it was becoming obvious that Kirk would have to be dealt with and in a permanent way.

Four local men were missing after attacking me and so far there had been no hue and cry over these people, but that could change if Kirk gave hints to the Authorities. All my instincts were to attack him but time and circumstances were not on my side. Long winter days lay ahead with all the attendant work on our farm to keep dry, warm, fed and maintain our stock.

Arrival at home was always a joyous affair. A big meal is prepared, with long earnest conversations with my Father about conditions on the road. I gave him a slightly amended version avoiding mention of attempted murder, but he's not silly and read clearly between the lines I gave him.

Whilst sat at the big table poring over my accounts shortly after returning, I watched Mother and Giselle in deep conversation and pretending to be studying my books, I listened to the following story as told to my Mother.

Mum asked Giselle what had happened for her to lose her parents.

It seemed she heard her Mother shout, "Giselle, quickly, ma cherie, hide yourself. The Englishmen are back," and...

These were the last words my Mother spoke to me that fateful day in Our Apothecary in St Omer, France. We had been visited once before by these ruffians demanding gold, silver, alcohol from my Father who had strongly resisted and now they had returned intent on getting their hands on whatever lay available.

We lived then in Place Victor Hugo and until the recent war between France, Prussia, England and Germany, we had a very successful lifestyle. Mother was English by birth but had married Father following, I gather, a whirlwind romance when she came over, with a governess, to visit the area as part of a minor tour. Father swept her off her feet at various dances, she fell in love and they married and worked together in the Chemist's shop as Mother referred to it in English.

I was born in 1798 and schooled locally and with private tutors as was the style at that time. By 1816 the battles had ceased, France and Napoleon had been defeated and we were reduced to a much more frugal lifestyle although Father always had money for essentials.

At dances and local meetings many requests to waltz and step the gavotte were such that I gained the impression I was attractive to the local young men. I have long dark hair, a smooth white skin, piercing brown eyes I am told and a slim figure of which I am very proud.

Horseriding is one of my passions and keeps me in tip top fitness. That and walking miles in the shop when helping as I am now familiar with all the Latin names of the many drugs, potions, roots and powders we stock and sell.

Twice before, bands of scruffy, savage English troops had scoured the town for plunder and these particular men had a most fierce disposition. Father detested them and was very voluble in his condemnation of them, such that they struck him very hard with their rifles and left him injured on the floor from the last visit.

We resolved as a family that on any future visits I would

hide upstairs in a small cupboard until they had gone. I hid as agreed and waited in trembling fear for them to leave. All remained very quiet down in the shop and my fears increased but then, disaster, my hiding place was discovered. I was dragged screaming out of the cupboard to a sight that turned my stomach to jelly. I was violently sick to see my beloved parents with their throats cut and lying bleeding on the shop floor.

Screaming, beating my hands, scratching wildly, I was dragged in front of the apparent leader and thrown down on the floor at his feet. He addressed me in English and demanded my name with slaps to the face.

I passed out.

I awoke to discover I was cold and very disoriented. It was noisy and slowly I realised the sound was coming from a moving cart, drawn by horses and I was inside and tied up.

Four long days I remained in that cart, held against my will and allowed out only for toilet and food purposes. Each evening I was imprisoned in filthy rooms by horrid leering men, fed, then locked in for the night. I wept bitterly, slept fitfully and remonstrated with my captors constantly and noisily. In the end I was threatened with rape by all four men if I did not reduce my wailing and shouting.

I have a good command of English from my Mother but only spoke in French to my captors and this proved useful. Gradually I realised I had been captured for a purpose and from snatches of conversation was to be taken to Northern England and then Scotland for a forced wedding to an older man.

Sergeant Kirk, the wicked despicable man in charge appeared to have fallen foul of the British Army for theft of money and goods from dead soldiers had been cashiered from the British Army, it seems. These men had joined him in robbery and theft on a large scale as they fled from the troops sent to arrest them, moving from the Waterloo Battlefield through Belgium and in to France.

So far I had been pawed and fondled but no other molestation had happened so far but my grimy state and filthy clothing and stench could have been a useful deterrent.

I demanded to be allowed to bathe and clean my clothing which was refused at first but by persistent demands I was given access to a bath with tepid water and a small piece of soap and in this way I cleaned up and washed my body and hair as best I could. Strangely, I was given some course rough clothing much warmer than my own fine linen and was told to dress in as masculine a way as possible. This I learnt in the execrable murdering of the French language they used.

Next day I was blindfolded but not before I had neatly packed my decent clothes into a small parcel to carry. Cobbled stones were under my feet and along with the usual stench of smoke and filth I detected faintly sea air.

Rough hands pulled me into a small boat and after a short passage I was manhandled into a smelly larger craft. Being blindfolded scared me to death but heightened my awareness of the surroundings. I was on a gently rocking boat.

What followed then was beyond belief. I was forced into a small cabin with a dirty porthole for the only light and I watched the shores of France disappear.

Four days I spent in that hellhole with minimum contact only for meals and to remove and replace the bucket provided for my sanitation.

Crying and weeping, kicking and shouting, I vented my intense anger and swore to escape at the earliest possible moment.

Smuggling boats regularly came and went from French and English ports and it was by this means I learned we were entering the harbour at South Shields, a port on the North East coast of England. It was bitterly cold and I welcomed the rough but warm clothing I wore.

That evening and for the next fourteen days, I walked with these villains across wild countryside and moors speaking to nobody as I was struck most heavily when I tried to make any contact with occasional passers-by.

In this weary and wretched state we arrived in a town called Dumfries. A cattle market was in full swing, people and cows, horses, sheep and even geese all over the place. I was locked in a room overlooking the market and watched carefully all the activities.

Early summer was here, the sun shining, crowds milling about and my anger at my capture grew and grew. I tried the window and found the sash moved very gently up and over. More effort brought the window almost fully open.

I examined the surroundings. Could I escape? This was the first opportunity to do so and was not to be missed. Out of the window, onto the ledge and I worked my body across to a sloping roof. From there it was a slide down and a jump to the ground. I was in a sort of back yard, hidden from the road and I moved slowly to the small wooden gate in the wall and peered out. Nothing ventured. I moved into the dark side of the lane outside and waited to get my breath.

Noise and bellowing nearby made me realise the market was in full swing and I hoped and prayed that somebody would realise my predicament and give me some assistance.

Blasted Sergeant Kirk appeared at the end of the street and immediately spotted me, gave chase and lashed with his stick until I screamed and cried in pain and frustration.

Suddenly the beating stopped. I lay on the ground, hardly daring to move when Kirk fell in front of me covered in blood and white with pain. I have never been so pleased in all my life. He lay still and passed out as I watched.

My saviour was a tall, dark, very handsome young man with the appearance of a very capable drover. He gave me his hand and gently brought me to my feet and dried my eyes. His questioning look brought me to my senses and I asked him in English if we could move away from the immediate area.

We walked together away from the market to an accommodation he knew was safe. He paid for my care and also pressed some money into my hand. Then he ordered me a glass of water and questioned me at length about my circumstances and difficulties. We spoke for over an hour. He was so very solicitous for my wellbeing and after a lot of close questioning realised I was being truthful and honest in my replies. He also appreciated the dire situation I was in and suggested he could help if I was willing.

This was how I met your Jack!

Mother's eyes filled and taking a handkerchief, she dabbed her face and then held Giselle in such a warm embrace that within moments they were both in floods of tears.

At last I had an inkling of the savage nature of Kirk and his cutthroats and resolved to protect this girl.

Marriage and all its preparations took care of the next two months. Banns were read in Church, the Service was agreed and a low key wedding was intended but then my three sisters and three sisters-in-law got wind of the proceedings.

Anyway it all worked out as good as intended, lovely bride, proud groom, bridesmaids everywhere, Ushers being efficient, the Vicar giving a few nice words and a week away together by coach and horses to Edinburgh.

Family occasions like this can be very beneficial particularly to my Mother who once again had all her offspring and their partners and children around to be made a fuss of.

Giselle was swept away by the sudden realisation that she was now one of a very large family and it made up in a small way for the lack of her own relatives.

Twice I saw Father in deep in conversation with my brothers and brother-in-law and I was a little put out that I was not included in these family discussions.

Back from honeymoon and the work of the farm took over again but I did not let that interfere with my smuggling activities and these went on apace. I suspect Giselle had an inkling of my nefarious activities but I had not yet been subject to the in depth interrogation I could anticipate. Indeed my wife had started to enquire about woollen goods and their purchase and sale so there was something afoot.

Giselle knew that most Scottish drovers and many of the English also would knit woollen goods whilst walking or riding with their cattle on a drove. In this way an additional income could made to offset the many harsh times that beset the cattle trade although the market had shown a steady growth despite the end of the Napoleonic War. Towns were expanding rapidly in the Middle of England with talk of an Industrial Revolution. Let's hope they all like beef.

CHAPTER 15
WINTER, TEA
AND SMUGGLING

Midnight on a cold September night found Dag and I
on a very remote track through the Eden Valley making
our way home after a bit of dealing in tobacco with some
local inn keepers. We had a lot of money collected and
some packets of tea for distribution. Providing you can
avoid the Revenue men, locals, thieves and other villains,
a good profit can be made from a bit of smuggling.

Reuben Connor and I had met up again after I had held
him by his ears and made it quite clear just what damage
Dag and I would do to him if he ever tried to trick us
again. I now believe he clearly understands.

Tea was the main trade I was now interested in. The
gentry who were ever trying to outdo one another had
taken to holding tea parties at their grand houses and
tea was very, very expensive. Yet Reuben could get hold
of a fair quantity which he reckoned was 'released' from
the bonded warehouses in Liverpool where he had
'connections'.

We'd met by agreement and having disposed of

the tobacco were heading for home along one of the remote high roads little used by traffic. Noises in the distance caused the dog and I to move forward with extreme caution. A single carriage light showed in the night and led us watchfully to a strange scene. A small one horse carriage had lost a wheel and the occupants were staring at the apparent disaster. Both were elderly and appeared to be man and wife, she dressed in a fine gown but he looking dishevelled, shirt sleeves rolled up and attempting to raise the carriage and re-fit the wheel that had dropped off when the pin to the axle had broken.

Whistling as we approached, the couple looked absolutely scared to death, hardly surprising when a dark haired man and a huge dog appeared from nowhere. The man attempted to stand guard but fell over a little drunk and his wife started to scream before I spoke, gave my name and asked if I could help in any way.

They both spoke at once but I held up my hand and asked the gentleman what had happened. It seems they were part of the local gentry, although in straitened circumstances and had been to a Ball in one of the local grand houses. They had been drinking in some quantity and due to the dark roads and unfamiliar landscape, they had taken the wrong turning and ended up on this road high above the Eden Valley and now not only lost but with no carriage to anywhere.

I listened with amusement and should perhaps have thought more carefully before I laughed out loud. The lady furiously upbraided me and worked herself into such a frenzy that she broke down in tears.

I was appalled at my stupidity and without thinking put my arms around her to comfort her. She stopped crying, looked at me long and hard and then in a whisper said, "Thank you, that was very kind of you to give me comfort." Her husband had climbed back on the road from his efforts to put on the wheel and we all sat and shared our thoughts.

My concern was the carriage. I undid the horse and tethered him nearby and examined the damage.

The pin holding the wheel on the axle had shaken loose and was missing goodness knows where. Slowly the wheel had moved outover and eventually dropped off with the result we could dimly view.

Broken timbers from the nearby woods gave me an idea and I collected a stout bough and used this as a lever to lift the axle and prop it up when I fitted the wheel back on. The previous problem remained, no pin to hold the wheel in place but a piece of hard fir tree was whittled down with my knife and made to fit.

Gathering the horse, I used it and my own strength to pull the carriage out of a small ditch and properly harnessed the horse again. All seemed well but I found both the lady and gentleman staring at me.

My left pocket had torn in the effort of fitting the wheel and sovereigns were scattered on the ground lit by the carriage light. They asked if I was a highwayman out to rob them.

After a long pause for very serious thought, I asked them to sit in the carriage while I explained. My name, I said, was Jack Rutherford, son of George Rutherford of Brough and I was to become a drover but was engaged in smuggling tea and tobacco to amass enough money to buy my first big herd of cattle. They listened in complete silence and I feared they would inform my Father and the Justices of the Peace accusing me of being both a robber and a smuggler, after all they were a part of 'the quality' locally.

Instead they asked me to accompany them to their home if I could show them the way and they would like to talk to me.

It took us an hour or more to reach their Hall that in the dark had the appearance of a fine dwelling with outhouses and stables.

We entered the house and they offered me a small drink after which they disclosed their interest. Tea, that strange leaf that I carried, had a huge social cachet for them. The people they had been with that evening had been invited back to the manor but Squire Jeremiah Ridley and his wife Henrietta were very short of money and could not afford the exorbitant cost of entertainment.

My mention of tea had thrown them a possible solution to the problem. We negotiated hard but I left their Ridley Hall with a handsome profit on my night's work and some good friends.

By four in the morning, Dag and I returned home. I hid my takings under Dag's kennel and slept soundly till woken at seven by my parents demanding I help on the farm. It was a long day.

So began a long winter and 1818 went and 1819 dawned grey, miserable and snowing, making New Year's Day memorable for its very poor start. But work continued to come in, occasional small herds passed through and our overnight stances and drover accommodation gave us a small income.

Giselle made it known to passing drovers she would be interested in buying good woollen goods and she amassed a small supply in storage. Once the Weekly Market started again in Brough as the weather improved, she intended to sell woollen goods both there and to the many passengers who briefly alighted from the stagecoaches to stretch their legs.

So we endured the long winter, and spring arrived with all its splendour of bursting new leaves, green shoots, happy people and to my mind settled prospects in our farm with its wonderful grazing fields and plenty of passing trade.

But then one night in the George Inn near my parents house in Brough, I overheard a conversation in the bar that sent shivers up my spine. I'd checked all my cattle and made sure the young men guarding them for the night were awake and alert. Cattle held in our stance were at our responsibility and thieves and robbers persisted in trying to steal from us. We live in very lawless times.

The George was packed, as usual, with locals plus

strangers from the stagecoaches, farriers, ostlers, farmers and drovers, the smoke from the tobacco filled the room and created a warm fug. Taking my pint of beer, I sat in a quiet corner after greeting various friends. As a drover, many were aware I would shortly undertake, in my own name, the hazardous movement of three hundred head of cattle to the markets in Northern England, indeed many of their sons were employed by me to assist in the drove.

My quiet sideline in selling tobacco, snuff and tea which I bought from smugglers was going well. It never ceases to amaze me how much social pedigree is bestowed by serving tea in the great houses in this area. Tobacco made me a lot of profit as well, providing I could keep ahead of the Revenue Men who had grave suspicions of me. Frankly, it was the profit from smuggling that helped me to agree the down payment on those beasts I had bought in Dumfries.

As two strangers staggered drunkenly into the bar, I realised I'd seen them with Silas Kirk in Dumfries and watched their movements very carefully.

Sure enough after noisily ordering beer, they casually looked round the room and there was an instant reaction when they spotted me. I left quietly by a little known side door and moved behind the bar area to overhear their conversation which proved to be a very wise move. Kirk had sent them to kill me, rob me of all my money, and take my wife and fulfil his contract in Cumberland.

So that was the plan and the reason they were here.

That was when I warned my Topman Duncan Brooks of the danger and asked him to increase vigilance on the herd we held in store. Duncan was a failed drover but still had his licence and against advice I employed him to drove my herd to keep within the law. Drovers can only register if they are married and over thirty years of age. I employ him on my terms. He will refrain from drink. Father also employed him as well on small local droves of both cattle and sheep.

Talk in the town taverns in Dumfries had confirmed my suspicions that Silas Kirk had been cashiered out of the British Army for the suspected act of robbing and stripping the dead of both sides and two companions, former soldiers, had also suffered dismissal from the military. Whilst on my drove from Dumfries, through Carlisle and along the Eden Valley to Kirby Stephen I had encountered others in my trade and packmen who knew of Kirk and his cut throats. One man reckoned Kirk kept a thumb complete with nail, in a bottle of gin to preserve it, alleging it had come from the battlefield at Waterloo. What a bastard. Some of his cutthroats were the two evil men dispatched by Kirk to bring about my demise.

Now with various of Kirk's villains effectively disposed of, I was reluctant to take my good fortune any further and risk being placed in front of the Magistrates again, this time for alleged murder but I needed a solution to my problem of these villains.

Stepping silently out of the tavern, I walked slowly into town seeking a remedy when I stopped to wait as the

Manchester/Carlisle/Newcastle coach and four rode past to a change of horses.

Hector waved from his high perch as coachman and I waved back disinterestedly when a thought occurred. Some short time ago I had visited Newcastle-upon-Tyne and found the best beer was served in the taverns next to the river.

On that occasion a sudden rush from the bar, late at night, with me included found us hiding in a nearby alley. A pressgang from the Navy collected those who had collapsed on the sidewalk from drink. They were whipped into a jollyboat and off they went for a very long while as reluctant sailors.

Hurrying down to the coach and its steaming horses, I avoided the ostlers and other horsey goings on and found Hector enjoying a pipe of tobacco out of sight of all the hard work. We knew each other from various fracas and he acknowledged now that I was quicker, stronger and more vicious than he so we got on well.

Questioned slowly and carefully, he told me there were two Navy vessels moored on the Tyne last time he visited, which was four days ago and yes, his next major stop after horse changes was Newcastle where he would have a full day of rest.

Once I had explained my plan, he showed interest that increased considerably when I suggested any money he found on his 'passengers' would defray any costs he incurred.

My only worry now was the likelihood of carriage

occupants becoming alarmed at our escapade but Hector assured me his four passengers had disembarked, with all their goods and chattels and were intending to catch the next coach and four to Edinburgh.

Wandering back to the George, I entered and took up my watch on the would be murderers who were quaffing a steady amount of ale, which was good. I encouraged the landlord to surreptitiously top up their pints and by closing time they were well and truly drunk, really staggering drunk.

As they left and took to an alley, I laid them out with my cudgel and then dragged them out of sight, bound and gagged them and went for our old wooden wheelbarrow.

Once in that, it was a simple task to cover them with a tarpaulin, put straw round the edge and take the barrow and its manure-like contents towards the coach harnessing area. Hector was waiting. We stripped them of any money and found £2.15s.4d which he thought would more than cover his costs, the lying scoundrel, but I let that go.

Once inside the coach, on the floor and out of view, we slightly released the gags, checked their bonds and then off they went to a hopefully watery voyage.

Three days later Hector stood near the farm and beckoned me over. It had all gone exactly to plan. Nobody had seen the men and the delivery to the noisiest tavern had disguised the sound of the coach and horses enough for the 'parcels' to be left, still full of drink, to be quickly picked up by the Navy and their pressgang. Hector delighted in telling me that once in the jollyboat and moving downstream, the Navy had removed the gags and the bellowing and shouting could be heard over the water for some way downriver!

Local rumour had it the ships were bound for the West Indies which I hear can be quite warm so I did them a favour, saved their lives and ensured a look at the world.

Hector agreed to hint at these events when on his travels and I had no doubt it would get back to Kirk and give him food for thought before sending more men to their fate.

CHAPTER 16
FATHER'S BOMBSHELL

About May time in that year of 1819 I had nicely finished settling a big herd in our stance and had placed all the drovers in our accommodation with the promise of a good meal that Mother and Giselle were creating.

Strangely, Father called me into the dining room and closed the door firmly behind him and bade me take a seat.

Our subsequent conversation turned my whole life upside down!

I'm the youngest of seven children and of course my parents are no longer young, in fact I was reminded that my Father was fifty five years of age and Mother was fifty four. During the long meetings held at my wedding it appeared that one of the guests, a close friend of my Father's, had made a very substantial offer for the farm and all its land.

My six brothers and sisters were concerned that I was using the farm without payment and was making a lot of profit from effectively 'their' inheritance. And they felt out of the equation. This offer, coming as it had out of the blue, had caused my parents to think long and hard about their future life and how it might shape.

Father had relatives in the market town of Penrith and a house and small garden there would fit in perfectly with their long term plans.

Was I in a position to buy my parents out and match or nearly match the offer that had been made?

What a shock this was. I had, perhaps foolishly, thought I was pulling far above my weight on the farm and had helped to ensure its commercial success over the last two years, so where was this leading?

Telling Father I was taken aback by this disclosure, I left the room to speak to my wife and together we went through the ramifications of this announcement. Long and hard we discussed the matter and realised that we were woefully short of the target my Father had mentioned and I now told my Father this.

Once I mentioned my predicament my Father immediately understood and agreed it would appear to be impossible for me to buy the farm and he would reluctantly discuss the offer he had received. He assuring me that I would share an equal proportion of the sale price after Mother and Father had bought a place to retire to and established how much income they would need to live on.

It seemed a funny way of going on but they were getting on a bit, I was after all the youngest of seven children and there had been pressure from my siblings to ' cash in' when they could and putting Dad in an awkward position. I have a long memory and will not forgive my brothers and sisters for that mean act.

On one of my visits to Ridley Hall to deliver tea, I had noticed large fields that remained unused around the Hall, that and a small servants' type building nearby had attracted my interest as a potential stance for cattle albeit a little off the beaten track.

Thoroughly depressed at my Father's news, I mentioned the Ridley Hall land to Giselle and she agreed with me we could do no worse than enquire if Jeremiah and Henrietta could rent some land and a building to us.

That day we travelled the short distance on horseback and we were delighted to see both Jeremiah and Henrietta at home and pleased to see us.

After greetings and introductions to my new wife we repaired indoors and I explained our reason for visiting in some detail.

Both listened attentively to my story and my request for rental on both the land and the small outbuilding. Without any consultation between them, Jeremiah announced that it would be a 'capital idea' and asked how we intended to go about it. Long discussion took place but at the end of it I had two very large fenced fields for cattle to overnight in although there were some repairs to be done in places to ensure nothing could escape.

Then Henrietta took Giselle to one side and they commenced a very long conversation to which neither I nor Jeremiah were included. In fact it went on so long he hinted we might make use of the time and walk his boundaries to discover how much work was needed and agree a rental price.

On our return, Giselle announced that we would not be moving into the servants' accommodation but would share Ridley Hall with the Ridley family and contribute equally to household expenses. That and the reasonable rental we had agreed made for a good afternoon's work and we left in high spirits to explain to my parents what we had achieved.

Father explained that while in town on a shopping trip he had been advised that correspondence had arrived with some recent letters delivered by the coaches as Royal Mail and one was addressed to me from the Solicitors in Stockton.

Opening it and reading it through with Giselle, it dwelt on our meeting and how happy the events had turned out and if he could be of further service just say, the usual stuff, and then he demanded that I produce £1900.0s.0d on the 1st of June 1920 or my interest in the riverside land would be forfeit along with my deposit.

This was a terrible blow to us and I was swept into the depths of despondency. No home, not enough money to purchase our farm from my parents and a huge bill to meet from the Stockton Solicitor who in fairness had warned me this may be the case.

CHAPTER 17
TO STOCKTON AND
GAMBLE ON LAND FUTURE

With financial disaster staring me in the face and the prospect of Kirk's thugs still prevalent, I went into a cold hard anger. There would be a solution. I was determined and Giselle and I discussed this for many hours when I hit on an idea.

Could I undertake a massive drove to the English Markets and make enough profit to meet my commitments. My cash holdings were now about £473 from the Dumfries venture and my smuggling had given me an income of about £47.0s.0d. A total of £520.

It would be an enormous risk in terms of finance and it was now early April 1819 so I would have to travel to either Dumfries or Falkirk, buy very carefully at least five hundred cattle and drove them to the York Market.

Thinking of the York Market brought to mind George Cook who appeared to have disappeared off the face of the Earth. What would I now give to have his calm presence and wise words right. I resolved to question the coachmen and packhorse men who regularly traversed the whole country to try to find some news of him.

Next morning I enquired of the various coachmen wandering around asking for news of a drover, George Cook and four dogs, particularly those who had travelled long distances from the south.

There was one vague mention of a man near Doncaster of that description but then I realised George would head for Bilsdale and Chop Gate, his home village first before coming to see me.

Giselle and I looked at my figures to see if they made sense. We had £520 to our name and I could not leave Giselle without any money and despite her arguing I had to leave her at least £8.0s.0d for the eight weeks I was away. I imagined I would buy in Falkirk, drove to York Market and sell that June giving me the chance to increase my income to cover my debts and be in a position the next year to pay the £1900 that was demanded. By my calculations this left me with £512 to buy cattle, pay tolls and wages and survive and it looked far too thin a margin. All this assumed a good market price at the relatively nearby sales in York.

Collecting my money into my saddlebag and packing some clothes before leaving I had to give it a go.

I felt a figure loom behind me and turned to confront an enemy, but dammit it was George Cook with a face wreathed in smiles and a good strong handshake. Where he had sprung from I didn't know or care, he was here and we started to talk together and quickly broke into laughter.

George had done remarkably well. Wintering in Sufffolk he had eked out a very frugal living over a long cold spell and then with the arrival of spring, his thin cattle blossomed enough over the next eight weeks and good demand at Smithfield Market meant he had made a profit for us. I stopped packing, grabbed his arm and hustled him into the house where Giselle was delighted to see him again and my Mother went all woozy because he is a very handsome fellow.

Sitting down he told me the tale. He and his four dogs had taken the scruffy herd of one hundred and fifty beasts first to Nottingham where there was no sale. He had vague connections in Suffolk and rumour was that grass was plentiful and nourishing. With the likelihood of a short winter, he could survive, just, and sell his fattened beasts at Smithfield Market in the spring. So he plodded on to Suffolk ending up in Sudbury on the drover's route to London and there his local connection paid off with an offer of outdoor pasture for the cattle and lodgings if he would earn his keep looking after all the farm animals.

This took him through a cold spell or two but the weather improved by late February that year and the beast quickly fattened and grew until by mid March with Market Conditions in London rumoured to be good he left, with hired hands and his faithful dogs and sold the whole herd in the London Market for £10.10s.0d each, £1522.10s.0d giving us a profit of £465.3s 0d. And George had called into York and paid our Letter of Credit already.

We shared the profit 50/50 and George gave me my

£ 232.11s.6d which I was relieved to collect and he was happy with his adventure and could consider himself a drover.

George asked why I was leaving and I explained my difficulties and prospects. We sat quietly for a while as George pondered and then asked if he could come with me.

Delighted as I was at that prospect, I had to put it to him that the journey was fraught with danger. Silas Kirk was forever on my mind but there was the prospect that if York sales fell through, we could end up traipsing round the country trying to sell cattle. He just smiled, reckoned I was trying to put him off and explained that there were two young ladies in Bilsdale who had set their bonnets at him, both were fiery tempered, somewhat stout and had a large family of big brothers keeping watch on them and now him.

Distance held a certain enchantment to George and he almost begged me to take him and whilst pretending a great reluctance, I agreed and we discussed how he would benefit. After long discussion we agreed to meet all expenses together and after I had paid out my dues the profit would be shared after I had cleared my £1900 debt for the land purchase. I don't think I have ever been so grateful to somebody in all my life. I hugged him like a brother and expressed my sincere gratitude.

His reply, "You gambled on me, now I'll do the same with you."

CHAPTER 18
SOLICITOR ADVISED,
OFF TO SCOTLAND

Whilst Giselle seemed to think the world of George Cook,
I got the impression she thought he was a bad influence
on me. We certainly didn't sit around quietly but entered
into a spirit of firm competition in anything we did and
it could lead to difficulties. He's a quiet bloke but very
handsome and that's where the difficulties start because
he always attracts the young ladies and their beaus find
this annoying and start a fight and of course I get dragged
in, but bloody George is nowhere to be seen when its
over, he just meets me later grinning from ear to ear. You
can see the problem.

Before leaving, I gave all my money from George
to Giselle, now uncomfortably aware it could be some
months before I would see her again and we cried a little
in each other's arms that day. But she was aware of the
life a drover leads and by that reckoning his wife as well.

We had agreed that she would move to Ridley Hall
when the sale of my Father's farm eventually went
through and the Ridleys were delighted at the prospect

and had insisted that in my absence, cattle could be held safely on their pasture and rents collected. The possibility was being considered of providing accommodation for drovers in the servants' building I had previously seen and Giselle believed she had enough spare money to convert it properly.

Buying a further horse for George, we settled our saddlebags and meagre belongings and set off, trailed by my wolfhound and four faithful collies.

First we traversed to Stockton, met Dyson Frobisher, signed my life and all my goods away in a contract to purchase riverside land and came away with a debt of £1900 round my neck, payable by 31st May 1820.

Little did I realise the stress that would create, fondly imagining the cattle would sell and I would be clear of debt before the end of 1819.

Our route from Stockton took us again through Penrith, then Carlisle and the drover's road through Gretna Green and Annan finally reaching Dumfries in five days of easy travelling.

More familiar now with the arrangements at the Cattle Market I knew that there were holding grounds much further from the town in the direction of Thornhill but not to far to be checked over.

Sure enough we came across vast holdings of prime Highland Black Cattle in batches of one hundred to one hundred and twenty at each stance and by my rough calculations we had to buy below £10.0s.0d and give a five per cent deposit down to succeed in this crazy venture.

Stance after stance we covered, viewing the cattle and checking prices but nowhere could we hear prices less than £10.10s.0d being bandied about. George covered one big area on horseback and on foot and I did the rest in a similar way.

Not a thing. Prices were clearly being held high by the demand and despite having a lot of cash available it was just not enough and the sales went through very quickly at £10.10s.0d and occasionally more.

George came over and nodded to me for us to move out of earshot of the many people milling around. It seemed he had noted samples of the beasts were taken down the road to the Dumfries Market and the price paid was dependent on the rest of the purchased herd being in as good a condition as those already seen.

Cattle sellers being the avaricious scoundrels we know about, quite a number of sales fell through when the rest of the herd were examined and we both wondered if we could exploit this anomaly. So we stood back and watched and sure enough, the bigger the herd of cattle for sale, the bigger the fiddle seemed to be. Question was, how could we take advantage?

I walked over to a big herd that George had previously watched and saw them selecting fifty good beasts and pushing them down the road to Dumfries Market. We followed in their wake and strode up to near the stand of beasts where they had been prodded and tugged in to a semi smart form for display. Nobody came near them, it was late in the afternoon and many buyers had filled their quota.

Biding our time, we lounged nearby and waited to strike our first part of the long bargaining process to follow, anticipating the sellers concern at no interest and aware they had a devil of a lot more beasts to dispose of.

Finally I moved over, viewed the herd and asked how many other beasts were included or were we bidding on just these animals.

"Well young sir, if you have the wherewithal, which I doubt, these are the poor end of a selection of many fine beasts from the Highlands of Scotland and I would be willing to take your money or Letter of Credit providing I can find out a bit about you or your Bankers if you have any."

So he thought me a man of straw and of no consequence, interesting, as he may well regret that remark.

"Suppose I tell you that that man standing over there who you saw me talking to was of the landed gentry here. Further, he has asked me to negotiate to buy five hundred cattle on his behalf, but at a keen price. You, sir, seem to doubt my ability so I will bid you good day."

Wandering off I signalled for George to join me and repaired to the Grapes for a small beer, making sure the loudmouth could see our movements.

One hour exactly from the time we left the man strode in to the tavern and ordered a small beer. Highland men invariably drink whisky, so the beer warned me he meant to negotiate so I told George to clear off.

Joining me and crashing his beer down, the man stared angrily at me for I seemed to have caught him at a short fuse.

"So what will you pay for my herd?"

"As little as I can," I replied, "and you will deal direct with me and not my companion who is not worldly with cattle. I will offer you £9.18s.0d per head with five per cent down and my Letter of Credit for six months."

He nearly exploded in front of me and thumped the table in annoyance. I just watched and smiled.

"I want £10.10s.0d for those fine healthy cattle and not a penny less."

I stated, "What you want and what you get are all very subjective and reliant on market conditions. Go and have a look at the crowds of buyers flocking round your herd if you want a lesson in market conditions."

"I'm the one sitting here prepared to negotiate but before I make any more offers I wish to see the whole herd and not these obviously selected animals and I want to do it now, so get your horse and join me outside."

With that gamble I withdrew from the tavern and found my horse and inevitably, my dog.

George came over and I told him what had happened and he confirmed there were few if any buyers either in the market or even now in the taverns where he had checked both outside for horses and inside for lingering traders. None.

Our Highland man appeared on horseback at that moment, nodded and we cantered off to the main holding area which I pretended I did not know.

Cattle were spread over the gentle sloping ground enjoying their rest from long travelling and feeding on reasonable pasture when we arrived.

I spent a good hour and more riding round the herd on horseback and my impression was a bunch of four to five year old cattle, hardened by savage Scottish Winters but capable in the majority of cases of the long trip ahead. Three weak animals I identified could be taken from the equation, now the haggling commenced.

We all retired to our various lodgings that night, no further ahead with the deal and agreed we would meet on the morrow and continue to negotiate. My last wish was to pay out any more money on accommodation than possible but I smelled a bargain.

Pouring rain greeted us the next morning putting an immediate damper on things and of course the herd looked very different soaking wet and miserable so I seized on this and commented unfavourably on their general condition.

Highland man's face fell and he looked askance at his field of woebegone beasts eating expensive grass and reducing his profits.

By about mid morning he was starting to see some sense, he'd come down from £10.2s.0d and I had eased up a little from £9.1s.0d to just over £9.5s.0d when he promptly agreed that price to my delight.

Enquiries he had made locally overnight had found in my favour and five per cent down was acceptable but payment in six months, 1st December this year. This was an impossibility as the word on the roads was not favourable for York Sales and a long drove may transpire. I needed a date of about the first of June in 1820 to coincide with my land purchase if all went well. I haggled and bargained and in the end gave him £9.8s.0d for each beast and a settlement of my Letter of Credit on 30th May 1820.

But he then demanded eight per cent down and not five per cent and that infuriated me and I was about to walk away when George reappeared, took in what was happening and reminded me we had a fund of £512.00 cash and the revised deposit of £376.0s.0d. still left a little for the roads and tolls.

Still fuming I shook hands on the deal and we repaired to the Grapes to the paper work and pay out my hard earned cash.

My revised Letter of Credit was for £ 4324.00 but now payable on the 4th June 1820.

CHAPTER 19
SOUTH WITH MY HERD

July of 1819 saw me about to set off on the long trail south to the hopefully lucrative markets spoken of on the road and that road was going to be a very different one to that previously travelled.

Five hundred head of cattle need a minimum of one man per sixty beasts so it would need a total of say eight men and I had George and four dog; me and my big dog and I needed a crew of at least five men who would come and go along the route.

We would pick up Duncan Brooke my Topman when we passed through Brough and until then I appointed George Cook to ride ahead of the herd to warn oncoming coaches and clear the way through towns and villages.

Looking round the market for likely crew, I made enquiries in all directions and it looked as though all was lost. Every time I found crew they were in the taverns drinking heavily and that was not going to work for me at all.

Wandering back in to Whitesands and the main selling area I came upon four Scotsmen, kilted, rough, hardy, my kind of people and I wandered over to talk. Being greeted as a Sassenach was bad enough and there was some mouthing of rude words in a strong Highland accent but I countered with sufficient vigour and in the vernacular that they smiled a little and questioned just what I had in mind.

They had come down on a big drove that arrived after my herd had been sold and they readily admitted they had few prospects of work at home and were seeking employment as they travelled south to better themselves. All were of drover families but the attractions of work in the industrial towns had caused them to take the huge gamble and leave home.

It took one and a half hours of haggling to agree a weekly wage for these rascals and I made it very clear who was in charge. They all four stood and challenged me but I would not stand down and a mutual respect was established; but very importantly, they all had dogs. Highland Collies bred to the work and more than capable of handling my herd.

With George leading, we left Dumfries and wended our way to Annan, Longtown, Gretna and slowly, ever so slowly we reached Carlisle where I put the weary herd to pasture in a halfpenny field, set suitable watches overnight and we relaxed for a full day to get our strength back.

Five hundred restless cattle create havoc along the wide droving roads and despite the Enclosures that reduced some of our route our herd would attempt to linger over any likely grass along the way and constant vigilance was needed to keep them on the move.

Like my crew, I walked with the herd, moving up and down to watch progress and ensure no strays escaped but I was encouraged to see the discipline of my Highlanders. They certainly knew their trade and worked tirelessly to keep a smooth movement and in one instance started playing some bagpipes which to my surprise soothed the beasts if not the humans.

In this congenial company we made steady progress, sleeping rough when necessary or taking cheap lodgings in towns and villages where we could overnight the herd in a suitable stance.

Carlisle was the point where the Highlanders would depart and I confess they would be sorely missed. Colin McLeod, their leader, came to wish me goodbye and asked exactly where I intended to go.

I explained my intention to sell in York if prices were favourable or I would move on south to find other markets but I was very flexible as a maximum price was my objective to meet my huge obligations. Colin had heard of Brough, my hometown, and showed a mild interest in continuing but decided against it, to my dismay.

We parted that evening with many a handshake and off they went, jangling my money in their pockets and making for the fleshpots of Carlisle.

Early next morning and with a much reduced workforce we attempted the long wide paths out of the city and it quickly became obvious we could not continue in this manner, we would lose a lot of cattle and we were in danger not just to ourselves but to any passing coaches as we were now on the major highway.

At the first opportunity I negotiated to put the herd in a large grass field, left George in charge and using his horse I rode quickly in to Carlisle to find a replacement crew. Coming out of the city I saw in the distance a bunch of men and as they came near it became apparent it was my ragged Highlanders.

I stopped the horse, they came reluctantly near and after a lot of muttering and chuntering in their guttural tongue the story came out. They had got absolutely, hopelessly drunk, squandered all their money or had it stolen and had been involved in a massive punch up in the town and against very heavy odds they came off much the worst and were left sleeping it off in a filthy gutter in a smelly back alley. Would I consider taking them back on please?

Suppressing a delighted grin I gave them a stern look and gave the appearance of giving this careful consideration before asking how far they wanted to travel and York seemed a good destination for them, so we joined forces again.

Meeting again with George and the herd we took the steady route and made Penrith, Eamont Bridge, Appleby and then to Brough.

Home coming, however brief, is always pleasant and the welcome at Ridley Hall was memorable. Giselle rushed to greet me and I swept her off her feet before making her known to Colin McLeod and his Highlanders.

Giselle took over, the Scots were placed in the

refurbished House, previously the servants quarters, George and I were prodded into the house, weary, dirty, smelly to be met by an absolutely delighted Jeremiah and Henrietta who claimed the house had come alive the day Giselle came to stay.

Hot water was put to boil, baths were ordered for us immediately and we came down to dinner that evening feeling much more human and normal.

Giselle had arranged a substantial meal for the Highlanders and hot water for bathing. She had bought all their knitted goods and arranged the night rota for the men who would care for the cattle. She told me she had cornered that knitted goods market locally in my absence and visited many of the local fairs to sell the produce and showed a decent profit. Not just this, but as a chemist's daughter from her days living with her late parents she had a little knowledge of drugs and potions and had acquired liniments and salves from the packmen and also sold these at market. Very impressive, I thought, and praised her acumen and foresight which stood me in good stead for a while.

One week later saw us set out again on the track across Stainmore and I warned my crew and Duncan Brookes who had now joined us, that we must maintain maximum vigilance over the moor as this was, as we well knew, a favourite place to stage an attack or attempt to thieve cattle. Funnily enough, all the Highlanders' eyes brightened visibly at the thought of a fight and a few short blades were surreptitiously sharpened as we travelled across that bleak moorland.

Nothing occurred. I thought I saw signs of being stalked from way behind but Dag was sent to investigate and came back somewhat crestfallen so there was no alarm.

But it set me thinking. Silas Kirk had not disappeared but would be watching, waiting to attack at any weak moment and I considered myself lucky to have such a hardy crew as the Highlanders who would put off any marauder once seen and assessed.

Bowes came over the horizon and we were able to use the same stance and have a good accommodation again.

Scotch Corner came and went, as did Catterick although the bridge there was affected by heavy flooding and we had a two day delay before we could continue. All this increased my wage bill and the toll fees now being charged ate up my funds at an alarming rate.

Leeming Bar, then the long, long trek to Boroughbridge where again rain made the bridge crossing a very slow business and of course an irascible toll bar keeper did not help at all. But we moved on through small villages and made Wetherby by the late July of that year, a little behind my hoped for schedule as I was anxious to return home and prepare for winter. Giselle was looking after about fifty cattle at Ridley House and we had enough hay but if they could be sold to a passing drover for a profit I would be pleased.

Giselle had mentioned a thing called a turnip, which I had never heard of, but she reckoned that in France they grew these things in poor soil and gave them as food to over wintered animals. I wished afterwards that I had taken more notice of her but at the time I was diverted by many other matters.

Wetherby was just like all the other places we passed through. Duncan went ahead on his horse and found and negotiated a price for us to place our many cattle in one or two suitable fields. He then agreed some accommodation and visited the town proper to hear of the talk on the road and any problems we may meet.

Alarming news came that distemper was suspected in the York Cattle Market and all sales were cancelled until further notice. My funds were getting lower by the day and this was indeed a severe body blow. Considering the very large investment I had in this herd there was no option but to continue to move south to Doncaster and avoid York completely.

Unknown to me at that time, our Highlanders had spotted men tailing us from a long way back but always keeping the herd in view and had left one of their number hidden in woodland to await the passage of these people and watch their movements.

First I knew of it was when Colin asked for a word in my ear privately and we drew aside as the herd moved on.

Two men on horseback were steadily dogging our passage keeping just sufficiently far back to avoid being spotted easily. They were cattle thieves, known to the Highlanders, and could easily rustle up to ten beasts if the weather conditions favoured their enterprise.

"What are your plans?" asked Colin.

Murder was out of the question, however tempting and we were too far away from the coast now to pull the pressgang trick so I suggested I would think about it.

Colin had an idea. He reckoned he was sick of walking and two horses between him and his crew would prove a boon on the road and a cash source once they left me; could they try an old Scottish trick?

I agreed immediately and watched the preparations with great interest.

Two of the largest and fiercest of the crew were slipped into passing woodland with stout rope and some muslin.

Afterwards I learned that they lay in wait for four hours patiently watching the road until the rustlers came by and when they were a suitable distance they followed behind until nightfall when they crept up, laid both of the thieves out and then stripped them naked, bound them up, gagged them and tied them to a tree.

Wearing some of the thieves' clothes they approached and secured the horses they had used, checked them over and then rode them to join our herd where we had settled down for the night. By the light of a candle in a storm lantern we examined each horse for distinguishing marks and finding none they joined our gathering.

Asked what would happen to the thieves, it was suggested they would get very, very cold and probably die of exposure unless they were very enterprising. Which they doubted. So much for Scottish rough justice.

Onward then day after day. We avoided York and made for Pontefract where we enquired about prospects at Doncaster Sales Market where again, rumours of distemper were rife.

Unwilling to risk my whole herd at Doncaster, we avoided the town and made for Ollerton, Worksop and then Newark. There I was approached to sell some of my cattle and the price offered was sufficient for me to agree and I released twenty prime beasts for £12.15s.0d which showed a good profit and gave me cash for my further journey.

Grantham was the next major stop and after trudging up the steep hill and across the high ground, the town came in to view as a welcome relief. Our overnight stop was extended into the next day as the weather turned against us and heavy rain fell. Our cattle didn't even notice the changing seasons or variable weather, they just munched on happily and ruminated noisily whilst enjoying such grazing as they never experienced in Scotland. This was a talking point with Colin and his stalwarts as we moved ever south.

Talking to George Cook, I asked him a lot of searching questions about Suffolk and its prospects because at this stage it had occurred to me we would not be home this winter.

CHAPTER 20
DECISION TIME

Long into the night I talked to George Cook asking about conditions in Suffolk, grazing potential, costs, accommodation and the likelihood of us getting paid work over a long winter to help us survive.

His long stay in Suffolk last year gave me an insight into the conditions we would experience over what could be a long harsh cold spell. My main concern was feed for the cattle which could become so costly as to bankrupt me and snow-filled fields gave little or no nourishment to hungry beasts.

George muttered something about turnips and a conversation with Giselle but I let my mind wander on to the long term prospects or lack of them and I became quite despondent.

I enquired about selling some cattle in Grantham and another ten beasts went for immediate slaughter at £12.15s.0d and whilst this was a profit, again it went nowhere in the long view ahead.

Packhorse men coming through the town were always a useful source of information and I asked about selling conditions elsewhere, knowing that major cities like Nottingham were within striking distance and could prove lucrative.

Distemper had been rumoured at Nottingham as well and all sales were cancelled there. So we left Grantham and moved the herd up and out across good grazing land and by early August had made good progress to Stamford.

In my heart I now knew we were to spend the winter in Suffolk and I would have to rely on George and his contacts.

George Cook, friend, traveller, drover, but there was a problem. Like me he stands almost 6 ft tall, blue eyes, blond hair, built very heavy in the chest but a slim waist and what I gather from Giselle, "Very Good Looking," and, as I've said before, that was where the problems lay.

Whenever we went into a tavern for a small beer or two, the girls wanted to talk to him, every time, flashing eyes, skirts lifted to show neat ankles, dropped handkerchiefs, the whole range of feminine wiles.

What then happens? As usual, some young blood felt the need to punch George and stepped forward, raising his fists. George just smiled and waited. Sure enough a punch would come, swiftly countered and then a brawl ensued, and I got dragged in because he's my friend. And who got the blame? Never George, he just stood and smiled, quietly nursing a bruised fist behind his back, whereas I seemed to attract all the attention and approbation. We kept getting asked to leave the taverns and all to the amusement of our Highland crew who seemed delighted to come and watch the free entertainment we inadvertently supplied but never got involved in the fracas. To be honest I was glad they sat these events out because I'd seen them in a real scrap and they took no prisoners.

Suffolk then and the decision made.

I sat and wrote a long letter to Giselle explaining our difficulty and the need to stay over to avoid bankruptcy and suggested she could write to me and entrust it to the coach drivers who all knew each other and would make sure any mail would eventually reach me.

Stamford behind us, we made our laborious way and came eventually to Huntingdon and rumour had it that a number of butchers from Northampton were making for the market to buy cattle for slaughter and salting for over winter.

I timed our arrival to coincide with the market the next day and found a suitable halfpenny field to keep the cattle in overnight.

Next morning Duncan and I selected fifty good beast and drove them to a pen for display and attracted a lot of interest. If my plan was to work, I needed to sell at least one hundred beast at £12.15s.0d or more in local markets to survive the approaching winter and the initial prospects were poor. Mine were by far the superior cattle having fed well on the journey down and muscled up to give them a very healthy look.

Not many cattle were on view and the small herds of five and eight beasts were sold very quickly but nothing came my way until late in the afternoon a coach came speeding up the carriageway and stopped with a flurry of horsewhip cracks and slithering hooves.

Out of the coach amidst dust and noise appeared a portly gent in top hat, tails and a rather smart walking stick. I had him down as a city gent but he strode boldly over and asked about my beasts.

He was a commercial butcher out of Northampton with a Naval Contract to supply salted beef. His coach had broken down, as they do and parts had to be made at the nearest blacksmiths, hence his delayed arrival in some haste.

All my stock in the market was viewed and then we repaired to the stance where the rest of my herd was grazing and a long slow examination took place.

Haggling started low and I made jest of his offers but we persevered and over a long afternoon agreed a cash in hand sale of one hundred beast for £12.16s.0d each.

We repaired to the local bank and after introductions and meeting the manager, this banker produced the cash for me. This gave me some thought as at all times I seemed to have large amounts of cash on my person, and thieves knew this better than most. After some discussion I decided to open an account there and keep the majority of my money in safe hands but keeping enough for living, wages and animal feed.

The butcher and I parted and he arranged for his herd to be driven away by drovers the next day but not before he had put a white lime mark on each of his chosen cattle, which seemed a good plan to me.

Huntingdon was left behind and we made our way along a broad carriageway to Cambridge which took the best part of a week.

It was now September and the nights were closing in, making long distances more difficult to achieve. We slowed down accordingly.

George suggested our destination in Suffolk would be Sudbury. This was the area he had visited with our herd the previous year and he had established some excellent contacts and knew of good grazing fields at a reasonable rated.

However, of more importance to me, the farmer/innkeeper who owned the land was reasonably well off but had no children to hand the farm on to and relied on contract labour to keep the business running. George reckoned we could work the farm business over winter, taking advantage of the limited accommodation provided, and the wages would give us sufficient to survive the cold weather.

On we walked to Sudbury and George went on ahead to negotiate our grazing for what was still a very sizeable herd of three hundred and seventy cattle.

At the White Horse in Sudbury we placed our herd in their two suitable fields and agreed a supply of hay to be delivered then wandered into the tavern which was part of the farm.

Lewis and Venetitia Stevens, owners of the farm and the White Horse tavern, made us most welcome and gave George a very fond greeting, asking how long we were staying this time. They were taken aback somewhat when I explained we would need accommodation for me, George, Duncan, Colin and the four other Highlanders for three days and then just George and I until the spring as Duncan had to get back to Brough.

Our discussion took some time and eventually we were shown and offered the use of a small outbuilding across a yard consisting of a single room with bunk beds in serried ranks containing straw mattresses.

There was a cast iron black leaded range with an open fire and water heating at the left side and a form of oven on the right side. A swinging arm allowed a kettle to be swung over the open fire or a griddle pan. There was a small protruding hearth in front of the fire to prevent hot cinders affecting the wooden floor.

Through the roof above we could see daylight between the tiles but we were assured it was dry and rainproof.

Within the single room there was a small window set low in the wall looking over the busy North Street carriageway. Lighting would be by candles and cold running water was from a pump on the wall with a long black handle. Rough, yes, but we had all been in much worse lodgings and at least we had a waterproof roof over our heads that beat sleeping under the hedgerows.

Our Highlanders were now briefly resting before taking the main road and heading for London where they had some prospects of work in the docks area so they said. We agreed a four hour rota for watching over the herd as rumours of cattle thieves had been raised in the tavern and ours were a prime target, particularly as we were newly arrived and tired from the journey.

Our rented fields were to the north of the town as the wetter meadows were not used until April each year.

My part in the draw for watch keeping was the first and I set off to carry out my duties from 8pm until midnight when one of the younger Highlanders would take over for the next four hours and then others until dawn. While the Highlanders remained with us, I needed to make use of their skills because in a few days they would be gone and the responsibility would fall heavily on George and I as Duncan would leave for home soon.

Leaving at 7pm, I walked in the fading light right round the resting herds in the two fields, checking on fences, gates and any other gaps and made a note to repair two likely places where the protection was suspect. By and large the herd was well contained and the pasture still fairly lush so there was a degree of content as I moved around the perimeters.

Long accustomed to cattle I made as little noise as possible as I strode restlessly round the area, watching carefully in the poor light for any undue activity among the beasts to indicate an intruder. Cows can be very aware of any unnecessary disturbance and the skill of the drover is to identify that incident and deal with it promptly and carefully.

Twice in the night I heard lowing from beasts in the part of the herd furthest from my then point and I made a quick return to the place where I had heard the noise, but there was nothing to see.

Midnight brought young Jock to take over from me and I warned him of my events earlier and asked him to be particularly wary, reminding him we were all sleeping only a hundred feet away and could respond to his call or whistle very promptly.

Dawn saw me first up. I went outside, splashed cold water over my torso, dried, dressed and went with my wolfhound to examine the herd in the coming dawn. Whistling softly to make Jock aware of my coming, I strode the ground I had covered last night and reached my starting point in about fifteen minutes with no sign of Jock but evidence of a broken fence and ground trampled by cattle. Thieves!

Running back to the building, I raised the rest and we hurried to the herd searching for young Jock and after some time he was discovered, unconscious in a hedge back, bleeding from a cudgel blow to his arm and head.

We removed a wooden door and used this as a makeshift stretcher to gently carry him to the tavern where Venetia and two young ladies took charge and one ran for the Doctor to come. I asked Lewis Stevens if he could look after the herd while we chased the robbers and he immediately agreed and Venetia said she would come with him after they had nursed young Jock.

Colin McLeod was not with us when we came out of the tavern but we moved to the trampled area and examined the ground, at the same time conducting a head count of the herd.

Fifty head of cattle had been forcibly removed and driven away in the direction of Washbrook and I had on my hands some very fierce and angry Highlanders bent on revenge but minus a leader. We followed the clear trail for a mile or more before a figure appeared and on approach we saw it was an irate Colin McLeod.

"I've tracked them to Washbrook and beyond," he said. "They are four men on horseback and seem to be heading to Ipswich and if they get to the port we lose all those beasts."

Without hesitation we all hurried forward into a steady trot that was tiring but ate up the miles and in four hours of hard slog we had the herd in sight.

Colin took over the coming plans for the battle. We were seven men, all with vast experience of rustlers and bandits and we knew there would be no quarter given now. If the thieves were armed with muskets, we would stand little chance with our staves and short swords but Colin had actually moved past the herd and had watched from a vantage point as the cattle moved past and no guns were seen.

Two Scots ran in a wide arc out of sight of the bandits to take a position well ahead to prevent any escape. They had short swords.

We five moved as one towards the herd, slipping around the side of the noisy beasts. One Scot sidled through the herd and had slashed one horsemen from his mount before any reaction was noted. Colin had made it absolutely clear that Dag would not be involved in this fracas. All the Scots had a wary regard for my Irish Wolfhound and from conversations on the road were aware of his abilities. But they had the distinct feeling he would not discriminate between thieves and Scots in a close encounter such as we were about to experience. He stayed with me.

The Scotsman who had slashed the first thief then left the man seriously unconscious behind the herd while a companion Scot took the unfortunate robber's hat, put it on and swung into the saddle from where he moved steadily to the next horseman and quickly dealt with him in the same way.

It was reassuring to me, watching this display of guile and cunning, that these warriors were on my side.

One of the remaining thieves rode back through the dust and whirling cloud to remonstrate with the errant horsemen and met the same fate. Cut from his horse by a savage blow with a short sword, he fell into the heard and was trampled to death.

One horseman remained and he stopped briefly to scan the herd, realised quickly that all was not well and galloped his horse away from the road to woodland nearby. I made to mount a horse and give chase but Colin indicated I should stay put and watch.

Racing into the trees on a clear escape path it grieved me beyond despair to see the robber escape.

We heard the rope twang into place from our view with

the herd and the runaway came to a sudden halt, headless!

Colin and I gathered the two bodies and the two prisoners were secured with ropes. Looking at the mangled corpse of the first man to fall among the herd, we came upon the idea of allowing the herd to walk over both the bodies which rapidly ground them into small pieces of fibre and clothing.

My idea of leading the two outlaws on the end of a rope behind a horse met with approval and so, after a very long hungry day we returned to the herd and handed over two very scared robbers to be taken under guard to the Magistrates and a Court Hearing in Ipswich.

In a very short time, we heard, they were tried and hanged and good riddance, I say.

CHAPTER 21
WINTER IN SUFFOLK

Colin McLeod, Jock and the other Highlanders left us two days later, Jock with a bandaged head and his arm in a sling. I was very sorry to see them go, they had been the most welcome company and very willing workers without whom I would have failed miserably. I paid their wages willingly and watched with a heavy heart as they moved onto the carriageway to London. Speaking to Colin the night before, I made it clear there would always be a welcome for them both here in Suffolk and at home in Brough, Westmorland, whenever they should need it. He was surprised and delighted.

Duncan Brookes, my Top Man, was the next to leave, anxious to begin the long journey home with his dogs and aware that he was another mouth to feed and a body to pay that I could ill afford. He took letters with him to Giselle and my parents telling them of our position.

I'd grown a beard. It was cold now and winter was setting in with a vengeance, ice on the water trough and we had taken to warming water on the hearth to wash in before we started work.

Our laundry was taken in weekly by one of the girls in the tavern that George had charmed and it was returned, for a small fee, at the week end.

Friday after work we dragged the zinc tub in front of the biggest fire we could make and filled it with water we boiled on the blaze. Primitive though the accommodation was, it had to serve as our home now for the next few months and we both settled into a routine of weekly chores of cleaning and brushing out and then the great bath on a Friday.

Dag slept outdoors for much of the time but would sneak in and lay in front of the fire at any opportunity. I allowed this now and again but much preferred him to be outdoors in a waterproof kennel I constructed and that way he acted as a very efficient guard dog.

Daily George and I both woke at dawn, washed outside in warmed water and consumed a brief breakfast of porridge or bread and dripping and light beer, the water being unreliable.

First duty was to check the herd and ensure their food and drink supply. Fortunately these Highland cattle were extremely hardy and would remain outdoors over winter and take no harm at all provided they had fodder and water and it was this that was eating very quickly in to my reserves of money.

Out of habit Dag and I roamed the area when the opportunity presented itself to look for fodder and I spent many a while gazing over hedgerows and gates trying to find suitable food for the herd. By the end of

December and the start of the New Year of 1820 the situation was becoming desperate.

Wrapped as warmly as I could against the bitter cold I headed in a new direction on my quest and came upon a very big field of strange round purple globes topped with lush green leaves. I leaned against the five bar gate and contemplated what on earth these could be and I must have mused for some long time when a very strange person appeared.

Dressed in the dandy style and very tall, he wore white boots, white breeches, a white waistcoat and a startling purple coat and cravat. His top hat actually had a feather attached.

We stared at each other for a very long time with no conversation at all until he suddenly burst out, "How dare you thtare at my navets like that."

Eying this caricature of a man very carefully, I resolved to walk away from what appeared to be the start of a confrontation.

Bless me, he seized my coat, dragged me closer and repeated his demand. "How dare you thtare at my navets."

This was a bit much and beyond normal country manners but I resolved to keep my temper, however Dag was far from pleased and bristled immediately, growling in his menacing fashion.

I was unhanded promptly and an immediate apology was offered in a lisping voice.

Slowly after that poor start, we made conversation. He was a very rich, eccentric local farmer and the owner, through heritage, of some eight hundred acres of the best farmland in the area. He spoke for many minutes about his high social standing locally, his friendship with the gentry, Magistrates, Nobility, in fact I was fast becoming bored with his boastful conduct when he repeated his demand about his blessed navets.

Slowly it dawned on me he was referring to the strange items in the ground that I had seen and on further questioning it appeared he was also a friend of a relative of Viscount Charles Townsend who was notorious for promoting the use of a foreign type of vegetable that was beneficial to cattle as well as crop rotation.

So he had planted a very big field with these items only to find they were shunned by beasts who would not eat the rich green stalks that were produced.

Vague memories stirred at that point from a conversation the previous year with Giselle when she had referred to navets as a fodder crop for wintered animals in France.

Curious now to learn a little more, I entered into a long talk with Jonathan Postlethwaite, for that was his name and I eventually obtained the story.

Viscount Townsend's relative had visited the area recently and commented favourably on the excellent nature of the local soil and had practically guaranteed that it would produce a wonderful crop of navets, or turnips as they were more commonly called in the area. But in a minor disaster for a very, very rich man the crop had proved unacceptable to the local cattle.

Luck plays a big hand in all our endeavours and being

in the right place at the right time has been commented on over the ages as turning the course of a battle, or in my case, the survival of my herd over winter.

Recalling Giselle's comments, she had noted that cattle in France refused to eat the green tops of these turnips but would readily eat the globular base provided it was cut into smaller pieces.

That was a very big field of turnips and if my suspicions proved correct then this could be the saving grace to feed my herd over the next few months but would they eat the stuff?

Mr Postlethwaite had turned and stared at his useless field and was looking most despondent. How could I take advantage of this opportunity to his and my profit?

Starting very slowly to develop my thinking, I asked how much it had cost him to prepare and sow the huge field with turnips and it appeared he had merely used a local ploughman to lightly turn the rich soil and planted the seeds he had bought from Mr Townsend.

By comparison with wheat or barley, his costs had been very low and his huge disappointment at the failure had cast a long shadow over his standing and acumen in the local farming community.

I was short of money, as always, but the thought occurred that, like my Letter if Credit to farmers, perhaps I could agree to take over this crop but pay for it in May when I had sold all my cattle.

So I developed my scheme very slowly and ran over each stage carefully and clearly. I would agree to buy the whole field of turnips, but only after I had tested them on my cattle. If the test was successful I would give him my Letter of Credit and he would be paid before the end of May 1820. It took some time, it really did, but in the end it slowly dawned on him that if I was able to feed my cattle over winter with his turnips then he would prove to the farming community just how prescient he had been and once again enjoy a good local standing.

My immediate suggestion was that he keep our arrangement strictly between us and no word should be given to anybody until after he was paid and if he failed in this I would refuse to settle my account. That did not sit well with him but I insisted on secrecy otherwise the crop would disappear before my eyes.

Eventually he agreed and with some reluctance we shook hands and agreed my terms.

Immediately I lifted as many of these turnips as I could carry and took them to the field where my herd grazed. Cutting off the leaves with my dirk, I offered the globe to the curious beasts who had gathered to examine this strange happening. Nothing. They just sniffed it and ignored the offering.

Bitter disappointment filled me at this refusal to eat the fodder, just when I thought I had achieved a major breakthrough.

Sitting down, I took the remaining turnips and slashed the tops off and in frustration struck at the vegetable, pretending I was beheading Silas Kirk. There was a sweet smell from the flesh that was revealed and the nearest beast lifted its head and lowed longingly, its head sniffing the air.

Hardly believing what I was seeing, I threw these meagre scraps over the fence and they were very promptly devoured! More scraps from Silas Kirk's head quickly followed and by the time I had sliced the remaining turnips and fed them, I knew I had overcome one of my major difficulties of winter feed.

Finding Mr Postlethwaite proved difficult but I eventually tracked him down to a local tavern and offered him my Letter of Credit very quietly and he accepted it after reading the terms we had established.

Once back at our accommodation in the White Horse, I brought George up to date with my news and he congratulated me on such a useful negotiation and then spoiled the whole thing by asking how we were going to chop hundreds of turnips up!

In my excitement at resolving one problem I had created another that would need some thinking about. We repaired to the bar of the White Horse and spoke to Steven in confidence and explained the problem as we saw it. Over a light beer we considered how best to feed three hundred and fifty cattle with turnips from a nearby field that needed to be cut up daily and eventually agreed to hire a local horse and cart on a daily basis, load it with turnips, take them to the field of cattle and cut them from the cart.

All this to be on top of our duties as farm labourers for which we were being paid a meagre wage and board and lodge.

Long cold hours we spent, snagging turnips as it was called, our backs to the prevailing cold winds and then with frozen hands loading the goods on to the cart, encouraging the horse to actually move and then cutting the globes as they came off the cart.

Letters from home were a most welcome link with happy times and the missives were read many times by the light of a flickering candle bringing welcome news. Coaches passed along the highway near our tavern and letters would eventually reach us many days after they were dispatched but having distant the connection with the Great North Road, coaches gave us an advantage of knowledgeable conversation with passing drivers who were always willing to oblige.

CHAPTER 22
FEBRUARY LOOMS,
MARCH BLOOMS

Sawing and cutting wood for the fire, keeping warm, checking and feeding cattle and farm work meant rising in winter before dawn to wash, have a meal, dress suitably and work constantly, with only a brief stop for a midday meal.

Trudging through the muddy fields we would see the carriages thundering by on the highway and dream of them whisking us back north to a welcome homecoming, all our debts cleared and a decent profit achieved. I think it was thoughts like this that kept me going through that hard January and into February.

Once the wind settles into the North East, it brings bitterly cold blasts from Russia and seeps the strength from all but the most hardy souls.

Thieving and rustling reduce at this time, snow leaves a clear pattern and direction to any missing beasts and the previous hanging had stiffened the local bandits into a semblance of normality.

Silas Kirk was ever on my mind however and my

vigilance in this was rewarded when two unsavoury characters walked in to the bar and enquired if we had work for them.

By their clothing alone we could tell they were neither drovers or of farming stock and we gave them a semi polite refusal. But they were resentful and vociferous in the tavern, calling us filthy Northerners and not fit to be working in their area of the country.

Steven, the landlord, was a big man and not used to this kind of behaviour in his tavern and he asked them to leave immediately. They would have none of it and remonstrated loudly that this was a public house. They had bought their beer for cash and would quaff their ale before leaving.

That was the day I realised just what was meant by a 'Suffolk Punch'.

I had always thought it was a big horse, but no, it was a well aimed deliberate smack on the jaw, delivered with gusto by an angry publican, twice!

Both men slumped to the floor unconscious to be woken by a bucket of cold water being dumped on their inert forms. Spluttering and gasping, they were thrown out into the night. That should have been the end of the matter but I had a suspicion they would be big trouble to us and I was glad when Dag, lying outside, growled his displeasure at their presence.

Some days later I saw these two skulking down the lane near our tavern and sent Dag to warn them off but he was late returning and I went to investigate.

These two men had encouraged Dag with loud words into coming through a hedge to deal with them where he had been promptly trapped in a big snare. He was slowly choking to death when I arrived and of course this was just as planned, my going to the dog's rescue would allow them to overpower me.

Dag is tough, very tough so I ignored him, drew my dirk and went for them in a fury of blows, punches, scratching and kicking and skilful knife work. All the frustration of a long cold hard winter boiled over. I saw the red mists again and I extracted a terrible vengeance on these two renegades, leaving them broken and bleeding where they dropped.

Using some twine, I very tightly bound their thumbs behind their backs in the most painful way I had been taught in Scotland.

Back at the hedge I broke through and cut the branch the wire snare was attached to, and slowly I released Dag who whimpered briefly then slumped exhausted to the hedge back.

It took him a good half hour to recover and he was intent on doing further damage to the ruffians but I prevented it going too far, because I had seen the fear in their eyes when the big dog loomed over them. So I joined them at ground level and started questioning them about their motives and leader.

Sure enough, after a little more persuasion from Dag, they admitted they were in the pay of Silas Kirk with an offer of £50.0s.0d if they could capture me and take me to him in Cambridge.

Shocked as I was to hear this confession, I realised just how exposed I was in this remote part of England and it was not unexpected.

More bodies I could not consider as questions would be asked shortly and Kirk would be the instigator. So with Dag as guard dog, I marched these ruffians to the White Horse where Steven and put them in a secure room and called the local officers of the Law, such as they were, and explained these men had to be taken to Ipswich and the Magistrates Court where I would shortly call and prefer charges.

Constant vigilance was my companion now and I thanked my lucky stars that I had such a firm and reliable dog.

Long cold days and I was becoming very disconsolate, stopping any passing coaches and asking for any letters or messages but nothing now for three weeks from Giselle and that added considerably to my concerns about money, feed and my mounting wages bill.

That evening over our meagre evening meal, I discussed the situation with George. We ranged over the constant threats from Kirk, my parlous financial position, rising costs for fodder turnips and carting and his own wage.

Late that evening we came to the conclusion that George would have to be paid off and make his way back home with his dogs. He reckoned to walk back to ensure his dogs were cared for although it was not unknown for drovers, after sales were concluded, to travel home by carriage and tell their dogs to 'go home' which they did and appeared at their kennels about a week later. It is a frequent sight to see a pack of dogs loping along the Great North Road, heading back north but stopping at frequent known taverns where they were fed and watered by a previous arrangement on the journey south.

None of this for George. He and his dogs would move steadily home and take any passing work on the journey, provided it was worthwhile.

His leaving was a bitter blow and I moped about for the next few days feeling very alone. Giselle was ever on my mind and the absence of letters made the feeling of loneliness intensify to a degree I had not thought possible.

How many loads of those turnips I carted from the field to the cattle is beyond my present state of mind to calculate, the one saving factor was that local labour approached me for work, mostly fit young men anxious to bring some money into their houses and the going rate was far less than I had realised. At home, a farm worker can earn £1.0s.0d a week but here I could pay 10d for an afternoon's picking, loading and snagging turnips which was a great help to me and enabled me to used two or three stout local lads to move fodder and turnips to my herd.

Turnips in the large field were now having to be moved from a much further distance as we used up the crop and the ground was now soaked and deeply rutted in the clinging mud. Challenging days and no let up with rain falling most times and further causing the fields to deteriorate.

Despite my having warned the local lads that in working for me moving turnips they had to keep very quiet about it, inevitably word got out. My countryman's skills were brought out when I noticed fresh footmarks in the sodden ground on the turnip field. Bastard thieving again of my bloody turnips.

I didn't need Dag for this one. I just lay for a long time in the hedgeback as only a drover knew how and my vigil paid off. They had the cheek to bring a horse with muffled feet and a cart to take away a full three tons of turnips.

Removing my boots and in stocking feet again, it was very cold but bearable. I handled my cudgel and crept up on them. Both were wielding very sharp slashers but putting the stalks in the cart with the turnips to ensure no trace was left.

Those slashers are nasty weapons in the right hands and I paused to revise my tactics when one of them moved in my direction and opened his breeches to piddle.

It was just so easy, one cudgel swipe and he dropped like a stone into the mud.

I took his hat off him, put it on and in the dark was able to get right up to the other thief and I dropped him with my cudgel as well.

Using the twine I brought they were bound up and then manhandled into the cart which I then led to the White Horse Tavern. Lewis and Venetia reckoned these two were from Ipswich and known scallywags so I left them out in the cold all night and then took them to the Magistrates in Ipswich.

I returned there briefly toward the end of February and I lay charges against all the criminals. Some I accused of cattle rustling which carried a very heavy death penalty.

The others were accused of stealing turnips and they pleaded guilty with a gaol sentence.

Back in Sudbury I knuckled down to the long hard days work with still no word from home despite my checking regularly with the coach drivers.

But word seemed to have got round among the criminal section. I had no more bother.

Sunshine greeted me on those early days of March, very different from the cold climes of Scotland and the high moors of Westmoreland and gave a welcome warmth to the days. It continued to shine, almost trying to make up for the dismal dreary days of February and, surprise, surprise, the grass started to grow. Only very slowly at first but there was a definite change each week encouraging me to view my herd with much greater enthusiasm as they grazed willingly on the fresh green shoots.

Which coincided with the end of the turnip crop, the whole field having been devoured greedily by my beasts who showed a remarkably good shape for over wintered beasts. Yes, I had suffered as much as any with the deprivations of that long cold period but the fodder and turnips had produced a very healthy looking herd of which I was justifiably proud and it was with that feeling of satisfaction still lingering that I made for my lodgings to be greeted by a smiling Venetia.

Coachmen had stopped by and delivered a parcel of

papers wrapped in twine with my name prominent on the label. Venetia reckoned the coachman was grinning from ear to ear when he came into the tavern stating, "That should keep him away from our wheels."

Letters from home at long last, and a lot of them. News was devoured that night by the light of my candle and I felt a close affinity to my wonderful part of this Great Britain. The Ridleys were well delighted with the increased activity that Giselle had engendered from both passing drovers and buyers of her knitted goods. Giselle had convinced Jeremiah and Henrietta to serve food occasionally to passing travellers and this had produced a modest profit. Tea was served at these events and word had spread quickly about the quality of the food and it was a venture they all three wanted to progress. So could I tell them how to get in touch with Reuben Connor as they needed further supplies of tea very quickly?

Page after page I read that night, feeling very close to my wife despite my long enforced absence and I realised just how fortunate I had been to fall in love with such a wonderful girl. Which brought me up sharp, thinking how vulnerable Giselle was if Silas Kirk came to that area again and in some ways I was relieved he was obsessed with chasing me down in this part of Suffolk.

Word in the letters was that my parents had successfully sold the farm and many of the grazing fields and awaited my return before they finalised the settlement of their affairs. Being the youngest of seven children, I had failed to appreciate my Father and Mother's ageing and they could now benefit from the result of their labours and retire to a small house in Brough. But it was still a very hard blow and difficult to come to terms with, being dismissed from the family home in such a peremptory manner. I would not forget it easily.

Right at the end of the latest letter came the most amazing good news that I would shortly become a Father! You could have knocked me down with a feather!

Straight across the path and into the tavern where I gave the good news to Steven and Venetia who were as delighted as I was. We had lived nearby for over six months now and had become very close as friends and for this reason I had just a little too many small beers and suffered the next morning.

Daily the warmth in the sun gave more and more life to the fields and hedgerows. During my early morning check of the herd and leading the horse and cart with fodder, I watched the early signs of spring with a growing optimism. Birds sang, crows gathered noisily, sparrows appeared from nowhere and thronged the road edges, and my cattle prospered. My letters home reflected this growing optimism that things might just work out in our favour.

CHAPTER 23
APRIL 1820

Alone now with only my dog for company, I ranged far and wide enquiring about hay for my beasts and the first week of April that year saw me cover many miles in search of suitably priced feed.

But that need ceased into the second week of that month when grass started to grow at such a steady rate that it became the favoured food of the herd. Indeed they thrived and put weight on at a very steady rate.

There was no doubt in my mind that the field of turnips had transformed my prospects immensely and I resolved to put this very point to Mr Postlethwaite whose foresight had made my venture viable.

Working quickly to complete all my chores and appointing two youngsters from the village to take care and watch my herd, I set off for the grand house occupied by the eccentric gentleman Jonathan Postlethwaite. Walking steadily, my dog nearby, I covered the three miles and came upon the house in all its grandeur and approached with some trepidation.

Giving my name to a butler who answered my knock

on the door, I was asked to wait and the door slammed in my face. Somewhat aggrieved at this, I turned and left only to hear shouting behind and when I turned, Jonathan ran over, pumped my hand and apologised for the peremptory treatment handed out by his servant.

We entered the house and made for an office where a large desk separated us but comfortable chairs took away the formality of the setting.

Explaining my reason for calling, I congratulated him on his tenacity and determination in planting a very risky crop of turnips that had never been tried in that region. He explained that his late uncle had promulgated the use of a four year cycle for fields which included clover, which I had never heard of, turnips which I was now aware of, and then wheat or barley followed by pasture on which animal manure would be laid.

Experience in Norfolk had transformed the ability of the local farms and greater production had ensued. All this was new to me but I listened and indeed took some notes to discuss with Giselle when I returned home.

However my principle reason for calling, I explained, was to thank Jonathan and confirm that on the sale of my cattle I would call and settle my Letter of Credit for the use of the turnips.

Eccentricity reigned supreme in my friend who dismissed my Letter of Credit as a nonsense, stating, "You have had the courage and strength of character to work almost single handed in feeding your herd with my revolutionary crop. Go away and think no more of your debt to me. You have very effectively proved my point and the local farmers will now pay heavily for my turnips thanks to you."

My heart thumped loudly at this comment. Could it be real? I owed this man a lot of money and he deserved it, very much so.

I remonstrated and explained that my word was my bond and I felt a need to fulfil my contract and maintain my integrity.

"Rubbish," was the response. "When you have concluded your sale of cattle, please call to see me and I will suggest an arrangement that will be in your interests and mine."

We shook hands cordially and I took my leave, somewhat confused but happy that I had both made a friend and fulfilled an ambition of a very astute man.

April days passed agreeably by and I gave serious consideration to the proposed drove to London. I would need experienced hands to move three hundred cattle along these drying roads and resolved to discuss this that night with Steven, the landlord of the tavern, who had proved to be a good friend as George Cook had predicted.

Approaching my herd in their present field, I saw my two helpers in conversation with a well-dressed gentleman on horseback.

Mounted on a magnificent black horse and dressed in a long coat, riding boots and carrying a horsewhip, he epitomised the local gentry from his high felt hat to his coloured neckerchief. If he intended to impress me, he achieved that in great swathes and I watched him most carefully as I neared, when he doffed his hat and remarked on the pleasant weather and the excellent condition of my herd. An excellent start to a conversation but I remained wary.

He had a wry smile on his face. "Come, young man, I am praising your enterprise and skill with as fine a herd of Scottish cattle as I have seen for some time. By trade I am a butcher out of Smithfield Market in London and I had heard rumours of a strong herd in this area and indeed Lewis Stevens is a long time friend of mine and mentioned your name to me."

Warming a little to this character, who did not dismount, I asked his business with me. His retort was interesting. He wanted to buy my herd, lock stock and barrel. Wise in these matters now, I did not jump in joy or show any reaction whatsoever to this announcement but kept silent.

Lewis, in the tavern, might have kept me informed but I would deal with that small matter later. Right now I needed to get the measure of this man.

I suggested we introduce ourselves, giving my name of Jack Rutherford to which he responded, "That is a strong Northern English name. I know of a George Rutherford out of Westmoreland. Could you be related?"

Before I replied, I asked, "To whom am I speaking?"

His response took me by surprise. "Arthur Collins," he replied, "you may have heard of me perhaps."

Many tales are told of the famous London butcher

who roams far and wide buying cattle at a good price but without ever dismounting from his horse. So this was with whom I was in conversation, and he knew my Father by reputation. This would need to be handled very carefully.

"Well Mr Collins, I'm delighted to make your acquaintance and gladly shake your hand. If you know my Father even by reputation then you will be aware I am going to be a very hard person to bargain with and I expect protracted negotiations."

This retort brought a very healthy chuckle from this man who rubbed his chin in contemplation before remarking. "I heard you would be a difficult challenge but I am in admiration of your strength of character in sticking out this long winter almost alone. Your Father was a hard man as well. Should I be willing to buy and you willing to sell then the deal would include all your cattle I see before me and I estimate them at about three hundred and seventy head which would be a very considerable drove to market. Would you be willing to assist if the price was right?"

"Providing we come to terms that I find suitable, I would not be surprised if the drove could be arranged but you would meet all the costs of the staff I would need to employ and of course the overnight stances and cattle feed on the way."

Again the wry grin and the hand to the chin before he commented, "Like Father like son. I should have realised. But what you say is reasonable and will be included in any deal as part of my costs."

We both stared at each other for a long time, neither speaking, just weighing up the prospects and considering, in my case, just what sort of price I could negotiate. Looking back my recollection was the need to have about £12.10s.0d per beast to make a profit and that would be tight.

"I have in mind," he said, "to offer you £12.15s.0d each animal and I would take you to my Bank in Chelmsford to collect the money in cash or notes."

Keeping my face rigid and showing no reaction, I pondered this offer. It would appear then that the large numbers of people looking for work in London had swelled the population to an extent that prices were rising rapidly at market and I determined to make the most of this fluctuation by negotiating very hard with Mr Collins. He was, by reputation, capable of a long discussion over price and I wondered how I could take advantage of this.

My suggestion was that we viewed all the herd together before we went any further. I was confident in the condition of my beasts and I wanted this to be firmly imprinted on his mind before we went any further. Plus of course this was the first offer made to me and who knows how many other butchers of repute would come along. I hinted at this as I walked alongside him through the two fields my herd occupied.

He asked how I had sustained the animals through the winter and was astounded when I explained about the turnip crop and its effect on the beasts. Again I had the impression this stood me in good stead.

Viewing the herd over, I invited Mr Collins to join

me in the White Horse for a small beer and a warm up over the large fire always ablaze in the tavern hearth. It might also give me a chance to question Lewis Stevens, the White Horse landlord, about this remarkable butcher person who accompanied me.

Small beers in hand we found a quiet corner. He filled his pipe and smoked a little and then asked what I thought if his offer.

"How long have you been away from London on this trip, Mr Collins?" I asked.

He reckoned no more than three days so I could safely assume the market conditions were perfect for him to bring my herd to London in a little over ten days and catch the Monday Smithfield Market Sales just as spring was breaking and there would be a steady flow of people into the capital looking for work and food.

With a straight face I asked for, "£14.0s.0d per beast."

His face was a picture of alarm and shock. "£14.0s.0d. per beast? You must be off your head, young man. Those prices were not reached at the height of the Napoleonic Wars! That's highway robbery. I'll give you £13.0s.0d and that's my limit, young Rutherford. You are trying my patience here."

"How many other butchers are there in this area, Mr Collins?" I asked. "Five? Six? You are the first person to come to me and I admire your own acumen but I am no pushover." I took a sip of my beer and explained, "My objective is to secure the maximum price I can for a very high quality herd of black Scottish Cattle now ready to be taken to market and sold to the highest bidder. You are in a unique position of being the first on the scene but I will not let that sway me from negotiating very hard with you or any other dealer, for that is the name of the game we endure to survive!"

Again the chin rub, again the long draw on his pipe of tobacco and after a long silence he made me his final offer. "These are my terms," he stated. "£13.5s.0d per beast and you deliver them to Chelmsford and I will pay the overnight stance costs, the men's wages and fodder charges but I will not pay you a penny more than this."

So, decision time, do I shake hands or seek elsewhere for another buyer who may not be as financially sound or reliable as Mr Arthur Collins?

I stood and we shook hands on the deal and accepted each other's word as gentlemen. A meeting was arranged at his Bank in Chelmsford for eight days hence when my money could be collected.

Two more beers were produced, we toasted to the success of the venture and agreed to start the drove in two days to give me time to conclude my affairs, hire some staff and bid farewells to the good friends I had made in this lovely part of Suffolk.

Arthur made a very sensible suggestion, £4902.10s is a lot of money in notes and coin and weighed far more than I could possibly carry alone. After a brief discussion, it seemed it was possible that a coach and horse could be hired at the Bank in Chelmsford and I could then travel by Mail Coach to Huntingdon and beyond.

CHAPTER 24
TO CHELMSFORD
AND BEYOND

Preparations for the drove took over my life for the next two days. Lewis introduced me to five strong local youths who would willingly travel the thirty odd miles from Sudbury to Chelmsford.

For my part I packed my few meagre belongings in my bag, dusted off my drover's boots, gaiters and long drover's coat and prepared to head out on the road again.

Farewells are not my strong point. I prefer to just nod and clear off but Venetia would have none of it and baked me two lovely pies and an apple tart for the journey. It was at that moment of departure I realised just what a wonderful couple they had been in suddenly accommodating and caring for eight hairy drovers and at least five dogs. Yes, we had paid for our lodgings and our food but we had only had the most friendly relationship and as my workforce slipped away they had ensured local men were available to keep me from exhaustion.

Tears were shed on leaving and a hug and warm embrace from Venetia and a firm handshake from Lewis saw me on the road again, surrounded by lowing cattle, my faithful dog nearby to control the herd.

I was most fortunate to have employed a rather older man who had previously been on three major droves, so I appointed him as Top Man and gave him a horse to ride at the front of the herd, warning coming traffic of our impending arrival so gates could be closed and dogs locked up. By listening carefully, the Top Man can anticipate coming coaches and horses and warn them to slow down although some take little or no notice and our herd scatter briefly.

Back on the road again I thoroughly enjoyed the changing scenery after my static winter and we reached Chelmsford in three days, well ahead of schedule to the delight of Arthur Collins.

Then the body blow!

His arrangements to join a larger drove to London had failed to materialise. Could he prevail upon me to continue in the London direction where he was sure a large well organised drove would meet us and take over?

Arthur hoped we would only need to drove the cattle as far as Romford when all would be well. Bankers in Romford would be utilised to pay me I was assured.

Only eighteen miles odd, according to Arthur, so we continued.

It was now mid May and I was conscious of the need to conclude all my dealings, settle my debts and make for home to conclude my river purchase, not forgetting to stop at Huntingdon on the way home and collect my money from the Bank there. By my reckoning there was £1400.0s.0d in the account.

Pouring rain greeted us after our overnight stop in Chelmsford and it took a lot of effort to get the cattle back on the road, but we persevered and started to make good progress. We left Ingatestone in the early afternoon and stopped at a wayside accommodation and cattle stance before again hitting the cold wet and miserable road to Romford.

It was at our overnight stop in Ingatestone that I found a nearby tavern and having set watches on the herd overnight, I reckoned I'd earned a couple of pints of ale.

There's always some useless hero that will challenge a stranger in a tavern, particularly if he's a big bloke and in his cups.

It happened, almost to a script in a book. I sat in a corner, drinking and watching and this burly bloke came over and kicked my feet, very hard. "Drink up and piss off" was the fond greeting!

I'm used to this sort of behaviour. They either sit down and watch or they stand over you, being, in their eyes, intimidating.

Doesn't work. I just sat and waited. Sure enough he had to lean over the rough table to try and get his hands on me. Smooth as silk I just pulled him nearer with my left hand, overbalanced him and hit him just to the right of his chin with a hard blow as I lifted from my seat.

Unconscious on the floor in front of me, I resumed my quiet drink, leaving him to slowly come round to a round of applause from his drinking companions whose smiles told me I had done the right thing.

Leaving shortly after, the landlord took me to one side and whispered, "That was the smoothest thing I have seen since I left the Army. Let me guess, you're a Drover. Take care, lad, but I think you have his measure."

Next day, despite my misgivings, Arthur Collins was as good as his word and a huge herd of cattle numbering more than three hundred beasts were swelled by our three hundred and seventy animals and put into a large adjacent field to our tavern lodgings for the night.

Arthur shrewdly commented on my swollen right fist, stating, "Word's got about and you will have no more trouble."

But this was now about the 19th May and I had very pressing matters to attend to in Huntingdon, Stockton-on-Tees, Brough and then Dumfries, and time was ebbing away far quicker than I anticipated.

Arthur Collins took me to his Bankers where I was offered payment in either notes or coin. I chose a mixture of the two and a Bank Clerk was despatched with some of my remaining money to purchase a strong box. On enquiry, the Banker knew of a tradesman blacksmith he used who made strong boxes to a good quality with a sound and reliable but secure lock. Shortly the clerk and a strong assistant came to the office and gave me the keys to a very stout and heavy strongbox, entirely suitable for my purposes. But impossible to carry on my own.

£4902.5s.0d were now held in the strongbox and the

only set of keys were around my neck secured with a leather thong. Or at least I suspected the only set of keys were in my possession and I asked the Bank Manager for the address of his tradesman blacksmith and requested he ask his staff to hire a horse and cart for me, which I paid him for and obtained a receipt.

Once the horse and cart arrived and my strong box loaded, I bade farewell to the Banker and a cordial goodbye to Mr Arthur Collins, very professional butcher of those parts. Two stout men carried the box to the cart and I secured it with ropes and took the reins, making directly to the blacksmiths premises.

Long experience has taught me the value of money and also just how many tricks can be played to ease it away from its rightful owner.

Noisy banging of forged iron greeted my arrival at the forge and after enquiries I met the maker of my strongbox and took him aside for a quiet chat. He was a big man as they are but a businessman also and he agreed that he had in stock a small number of very heavy duty locks and keys similar to that installed on my strongbox. We agreed, after discussion, to change the lock on my box for a fresh mechanism, slightly more sophisticated than the previous one with two more tongues on the key and additional levers in the new lock to match.

Revealing only as much as I thought necessary, I opened the box in a separate room and watched as the smith removed the previous mechanism and replaced it with the new one I had purchased. Once tested I made the unusual, to him, request for a second set of keys to be cut and this took all of two hours but in the end both fitted to my entire satisfaction.

CHAPTER 25
THE LONG ROAD NORTH

Romford is a busy coaching town on the main road to London and in a short time my horse, cart and inevitable dog found the busy area where horses, men, coaches and bewildered passengers mingled.

My enquiries revealed that my box and I could be accommodated easily but under no circumstances whatsoever would my faithful hound be permitted in, on, or near the coach. That was a huge setback to my plans and I moved away from curious eyes to consider my options.

Cattle constantly moving through the town would indicate drovers in the vicinity, many of them from Scotland or Northern England now making their way home by road and taking their dogs with them. It is a habit in the droving trade to return home by coach if very successful and demand the dogs to, "Go home," which remarkably they do. Could I use this to get Dag back home?

Once on the main road again, it was only after roughly an hour's waiting that a band of kilted warriors appeared, swaggering along and surrounded by dogs of all shapes and sizes but principally sheep dogs.

Catching the eye of the most fierce of the Scots, I established my credentials as a drover and they eyed my strong box with greedy expressions. I threatened violence and the leader brought his men quickly to order.

Negotiating took but a moment. I gave Dag's lead to the man and paid a small sum for the dog's feed and care which vanished like lightning into his sporran. He knew Brough in Westmoreland and would leave the dog in the town to find me, knowing he knew I would reach Ridley Hall eventually.

With a very heavy heart, I watched my constant companion depart and his soulful backward glance was distressing to me, such that I quickly gathered the reins of the cart horse and, hiding my damp cheeks, made for the coaching station again. Alone and carrying far more money than was wise, I allowed the horse to bring me at a steady pace to where the coaches gathered their fares.

Talking to the ostlers nearby, I learned that my best route would be to make for the outskirts of London, then take a coach to Cambridge and then change there to go west to Huntingdon where I could visit my Bank and collect the balance of my money.

It was now the 21st May and I estimated four days' travel to enable me to reach Stockton-on-Tees to meet my first deadline of the 1st June but there was little leeway and bad weather or a breakdown could affect the whole timetable.

We set off for London that early evening with the prospect of catching the northbound fast coach to Cambridge as it left London. I made certain my heavy strongbox was secured safely before entering the crowded coach and assessing my travelling companions but all seemed greatly wearied by their journey so far and there was little talk among us.

Nearing central London, my small tip to the driver paid handsome dividends when he called my attention from his high position on the box and advised I should be ready to leave the coach in a few moments. He had spotted heavy dust in the distance and was sure it would be my coach travelling to not Cambridge but along the Great North Road direct through almost to Huntingdon.

Using his horn he attracted the attention of the nearing coach which stopped and I made a hasty exit and was helped to move my strongbox by the coachman and his assistant where we installed it securely on the northbound coach and I mounted gratefully into a carriage much less crowded that the previous one.

In one corner a bewhiskered gentleman and me, and opposite a husband and wife patently on their first coach trip and staring fixedly out of the window at the passing countryside in the fading light.

Sleep comes to me very easily possibly because of my occupation and its outdoor life and I was heartily glad of this as the coach rolled ever northwards, stopping every twenty two miles or so for a change of horses and a chance to stretch tired legs.

Fourteen uncomfortable hours later saw me deposited on the streets of St Neot's with my precious strongbox and few people moving about at midday. Moving to the nearest tavern, I ordered a beer and enquired of the nearest stables.

The landlord looked at me with a jaundiced eye and asked how I would pay and it was then I realised just what a disreputable state I was in, having been tossed about on the damned stagecoach. I explained this and produced a little money. He eyed me and my strongbox very carefully, having watched me and two hired men carry it in but the money spoke loudly and he agreed to provide me with transport to the livery stable.

Once there I was made aware they would not allow me a horse to carry such a load and suggested the coach again.

More time wasted as, with hired help, I trudged to the coach station and arranged a 3pm place, with my baggage, to Huntingdon.

Sleeping briefly sitting on my strongbox, I was woken and advised to move quickly if I wished to go to Huntingdon and boarded for the journey. Three hours later saw me alight near the Bank which was closed for the night. More delay.

Finding accommodation nearby I had a meal and returned to my room to sleep the sleep of the just, or in my case the extremely tired and frustrated.

Nine thirty next day saw me with a hired horse and cart parked up outside and waiting for the Bank to open. Promptly at 9.30am, the doors opened and I asked to see the Manager. To my astonishment they refused. It appeared my dress and general appearance had put the clerk off and I was asked to leave.

Catching two large men nearby once I was outside, I paid them a tip and we lifted my strong box and placed it right across the entrance to the Bank, completely blocking the way in and way out.

After that I just sat on the box and waited. First the doorman came out and remonstrated. I ignored him, then the fussy clerk came out and requested I leave promptly. I gave him a piece of my mind, he blushed and ran indoors. Finally the Manager appeared, took one look at me and my obvious box of valuables and was all apologies.

How could he make amends for such a valuable client? I was ushered into his office, fussy bottom was told to make me some tea and the bank doorman was deputised to move my box into the building and guard it with his life.

All that fuss had created quite a crowd and although I achieved my objective in seeing the Manager and getting my money, it had an unforeseen consequence.

This Bank Manager was remote from London and had no real idea of my standing or background. Over tea I asked about a secure place for some of my valuables and a safe box in the bank vaults sounded the perfect solution. After paying a small fee, I was left alone with my box, one key being mine, the other held by the Bank and a secure code word established. Alone in the room I put the spare keys to my strong box in the container, then the Manager and I locked the thing, and into the vault it went for safe keeping.

Nothing left then but to collect my money, this time in £1 notes which were much lighter and at the Manager's suggestion the strongbox was shuffled into his office and I exchanged a lot of the heavy coin for these £1 notes and that made my task of moving the box much easier. Again I took a receipt.

Returning to my accommodation, I announced my early departure on the 6am coach running from Huntingdon and along the route of the Great North Road. Then a meal and an early night to be as fresh as possible for the next morning and I arranged to have some bread and water available as I left and settled my bill that night before retiring.

24th May at 5am saw me and my much lighter strongbox being accompanied to the coach station as the tavern had produced a man and a wheelbarrow to move my goods.

Six in the morning saw the coach move away from the town and I settled down alone, my feet on the strong box and contemplated my next urgent actions.

Time was not on my side, a two day non-stop journey lay ahead and it was now late May so with reasonable luck I would reach Stockton on the 26th May in good time to meet my 1st June deadline.

CHAPTER 26
SILAS KIRK

With some £6000 in mostly notes contained in my strongbox, I was happy to have it at my feet, the coach being surprisingly empty.

Moving steadily through the long early summer day, the swaying motion and my extreme exhaustion made sleep a very comfortable option and I dozed fitfully for many miles.

Four horse changes later and having had company on some of the stages, I was once again alone in the carriage about one hundred miles into my non-stop journey when I heard the fateful words, "Stand and deliver."

Highwaymen.

None other than Silas Kirk appeared at the window and his delight at seeing me and my strongbox was matched by my dismay and exasperation. Reaching for my dirk, I was stopped in my movements by the large calibre pistol that appeared in his hand aimed at my face.

Slowly, very slowly, he reached and took my dirk and pocketed it.

His companion came in the carriage door behind me

and seized my arms and wrapped a rope around me and then the coach driver appeared, grinning at my plight, and it was then I realised they must have followed my movements from the outskirts of London and despite my vigilance they had outwitted me.

No good could come of this meeting. They had chosen a remote location and in my peripheral vision I spotted a broken cottage where they eventually dragged me, kicking and fighting but to no avail.

Once inside I was savagely beaten by a limping Kirk and his two villains who found every way possible to inflict maximum pain.

Without food or water, my boots were removed, my keys were taken from me and the strong box opened with the contents being viewed by Kirk and his companions with a reverence filled with greed and avarice. Noting this, I reckoned Kirk would have a few problems with these two and that may be a weakness I could exploit.

Cold and hunger should have overtaken me but anger superseded, cold hard killing anger such as I have never known in my life.

I have killed men who attacked me and while regretting the loss of life, if it was a choice between them or me, as had often happened, there was no doubt I would make every effort to win.

Whilst beating me, Kirk had constantly asked about his former soldier companions sent to kill me and I refused to talk. This only increased the ferocity of his attacks but I remained silent. There was nothing to stop them killing me now. They had my money and the keys to the box but Kirk had this strange need to know about his men and I would use that to remain alive a little longer.

Hands and feet securely tied and a gag across my mouth to stop me bleeding from broken teeth, I felt wretched at being so close to success and a bitter gall filled my being as I lay in pain into that cold night.

After midnight and a little painful sleep, I put my mind to escape and considered carefully my surroundings. There was a stone rubble floor, a broken window letting in very little light and a largely missing roof and it was that roof and its missing tiles that gave me some faint hope.

Scrabbling round on the floor as best I could, I searched the whole room and found nothing of use, but moving again to my corner a slight snick on my arm identified for me by feel a small piece of roof tile embedded in the rough clay and gravel floor of the room.

Twisting and turning I managed to get my tied hands over the shard and commenced sawing at my bonds and I could feel the rope giving way very slowly strand by strand.

Then disaster. Somebody coming. It was one of Kirk's henchmen, checking on me by the light of a flickering candle.

Leering in the dark, he described in minute detail just what Kirk intended to do to me with a hot sharp knife until he had the detail of every single person he had sent against me and their fate. I kept silent, so he kicked me in the side and left me writhing in agony and groaning.

In truth I felt the blow but I've suffered far worse from an irate cow, but he seemed delighted at his ability to inflict pain and went away laughing.

Once the pain subsided I started again on my bonds and after many anxious moments felt the final strands slip apart. I was numb from the very tight rope and the feeling came back very gradually to my aching limbs. But come back it did and in short order I had undone the rope round my ankles and was free.

Of course once I checked I found the door locked but I now had a sort of weapon in the rope used to bind me and using my skills I fashioned a noose to help me to quickly strangle the next visitor.

During the night they had checked on me roughly every two hours by my calculations so I waited patiently for the next visit.

I needed that door unlocked to achieve my escape but not before at least one man was down and away from fighting me.

Lying as before I made use of bits of rope to give the impression of being tied up but I had the strangling noose under my back out of sight.

Almost asleep, despite my predicament, I was supine when the next visitor came but he made the serious mistake of bending down to check I was alive. Like a snake I struck him under the jaw and he gagged and fell. Within seconds and despite my wounds, I had the noose round his neck and he finally stopped kicking and had no pulse to my touch.

In his pocket he had my precious dirk and little coin but that was a weapon I didn't have previously.

Some noise must have penetrated to the other side of the house as I heard movement and my previous tormentor was heard approaching, telling me just what a kicking I could expect this time.

Entering noisily, he moved across to aim a kick at his fallen companion when I came silently from behind and put the small dirk straight into his throat. It was not enough to kill him but it stopped him in his tracks in sheer horror. Then I closed and locked the door and stalked him in that now quiet room. He whimpered then, swearing he would kill me before he bled to death and then suggested he had never meant to hurt me and would help me escape.

Ruthlessly I stalked him through that little room. Every time he moved so did I and his body language told me I had cut some vital artery in his neck, the floor becoming damp with his blood.

I waited for my moment then hit again with the dirk, but this time to his side and aimed for his heart but the blade was just too short and he wheezed out of my reach.

Sickened by this torture I found the rope while my assailant was at the other end of the room and moved in quickly and strangled him. He struggled desperately for moments and then went limp and I knew he was dead.

No real weapons on this one either, just another short knife which I pocketed, then a search with the candle, and I found and donned my boots.

Now for Silas Kirk and this had been a long time

in coming to fruition and my killer instincts, honed in Scotland, would be put to the ultimate test.

Searching very silently round the house, I could discover no trace of the rascal but then noises of harness jingling reminded me these thugs had stolen a coach and horses and that would be Kirk's escape route.

Skirting the house in the dark, I moved as quietly as possible to the sound of horses and harness creaking and was some yards away when the coach and horses moved away. I ran as fast as my wounds would let me and in a desperate leap landed on the rear of the coach and clung on for dear life.

Some long distance from the scene of my captivity, Kirk must have thought himself clear and slowed down to a trot. Grasping on to anything my hand touched in the inky blackness, I crept painfully up the back of the coach and slithered across the roof.

Kirk was standing in the driving position and ignoring the seat normally used by the coach driver. I had the immediate impression he was out of his depths with a coach and four. He had to keep a tight grip of the four reins or lose the coach on the road verge.

To say he was surprised at my appearance would be an understatement, he practically shat himself and stood mesmerised, holding reins in both hands and practically helpless.

I must have presented an awesome sight, covered in blood, both my own and that of my assailants, and he would now be in no doubt as to his own fate.

"What an overgrown heap of tripe you are, Kirk," I said conversationally. "You are the most evil bastard it has ever been my misfortune to come across. I am your Nemesis and I intend to take extreme measures right now."

So I just pushed him under the wheels.

His face, as he fell, went very quickly through the emotions of alarm, despair and then a screaming wail cut off by the wheels.

I stopped the horses, tied them securely to prevent them careering away and made sure my strongbox was in the coach before I released the horses and in the gradually lightening sky I made steady progress back through to Stamford where I estimated the coach had been stolen from.

There was a huge hullabaloo when we came in sight of the town for word had spread that thieves and robbers had stolen the coach and left passengers stranded in the town. Straight to the coach station I slowly drove the horses and dropping with tiredness and now bleeding from various cuts, I told my story and produced the intact strongbox.

Recommended to the nearest Blacksmith, I watched as the hasp was cut in my strongbox and I could verify that nothing had been removed. I paid the Smith to put a temporary hasp on and bought an old padlock and two keys.

Desperate as I was for rest and sleep, my only thought was to reach Stockton in time to prevent my land option being forfeit. Explaining my dilemma to a very grateful owner of the coach and horses, he asked what my time factor was and that brought me to a stop.

"What date it is it please?" I asked.

25th May 1820 was the truly alarming reply.

Staring at my dishevelled person and noting my bleeding wounds, he suggested an immediate visit to the Doctor, but I had a hundred and forty miles to cover in five days and that was a near impossibility. Then I considered the huge risks I had taken to get this far and took the decision to move on using some of the money from my strongbox to pay for a rapid transfer to Stockton.

Coach owners are ever willing to listen to money talking and we agreed a price to get me as far as Wetherby where the regular coach would take me the rest of the way. Once we agreed a price of £10.0s.0d, he gave me £5.0s.0d back for my bravery and safe recovery of his coach and valuable horses.

Following a brief visit to the Doctor to be patched up, my damned strongbox and I left at 10am and I commenced the long weary and painful journey to Wetherby where we arrived thirty hours later having stopped each twenty three miles for a change of horses.

CHAPTER 27
TO STOCKTON

Rain soaked streets greeted me on arrival in Wetherby that May morning in early summer. It was the 28th May now by my fuddled brain. Alighting from the coach and collecting my strong box, I noticed a branch of the Yorkshire District Bank that had just opened its doors and merely looking at the huge box I was carting about the country set me to thinking about the weight alone and the idea struck!

Soaked to the skin by now, I dragged the cursed box into the Bank and asked to see the Manager. Swiftly the bank clerk assessed my social standing as 'poor' but the large and very obvious strongbox caused him to reassess and the Manager was summoned.

Once in his office, his staff having heaved and struggled to bring my box along, we started proceedings... Who was I? Where was I from? What, if any, credentials had I? And what was in that big box? Good start.

Without pause I asked him to lock his office door and proceeded to open the chest. Eyes jumping out of his head, he slowly rose from behind his desk and approached my hoard.

"To whom does all this coin and paper money belong?" he enquired and I gave him a detailed explanation over the next fifteen minutes or so and produced receipts for the money I had paid out.

"So you want to exchange all that heavy coin for paper money and clear me out of all my stock, young man. Just how much money are you carrying in that strongbox?"

"There's £6,303.5s.0d in that box and it's all counted and correct. So are you prepared to help me?"

Without more ado two clerks were summoned and in my and the Manager's presence counted out all the coin to a total of £1023.5s.0d and I was offered £1.0.0 notes as replacement.

Quickly the manager summoned a young lady, gave her some money and sent her on an errand from which she quickly returned with a handsome large leather satchel. I realised just how perfect this would be to transport my money and awaited developments and sure enough the bag was offered to me to use, provided I left my strongbox with the Manager in exchange. It made sense and I accepted promptly, giving him the keys from round my neck and we watched the paper money swell the satchel which had a stout lock on its opening flap.

We exchanged keys and receipts then I mentioned that a spare set of keys existed for the former padlock which was now redundant.

This alarmed him greatly, until I mentioned they were in a Bank in Romford and I gave him the secret code we had established, which the Manager felt would be completely in order if he needed to write and check on my credentials

Greatly relieved and with my satchel over my shoulder, I was able to make good speed on the drying road to the coach gathering area and caught the next available one to traverse once again on the Great North Road.

Time was now of the essence. All these enforced delays and lack of proper sleep were telling on me. I was exhausted and still wounded badly.

Once safely aboard the coach, we maintained the five miles per hour pace and including the various stops for a change of horse we arrived in Yarm-on-Tees by midnight, hoping to reach Stockton just five miles hence but no coaches were going that evening or indeed the next day, so I was informed.

What on Earth could possibly delay me now? What a terrible disappointment and so close to my goal.

Had I been in good health I would have walked the distance but I just had to find a tavern, feed and have a good night's sleep. My wounds and total exhaustion made me look for lodgings.

At the Ketton Ox tavern, I ate a hastily prepared meal and retired to my room on the upper floor.

At 9am on the 1st June 1820, I had to be in the office of my Solicitor in Finkle Street, Stockton, or forfeit my £100 deposit and with these thoughts tumbling through my head I slept soundly. I woke to heavy rain on the windows and water gushing noisily through the metal downcomers.

Yarm floods… Very frequently.

Through the window I could see outside that the river water was rising rapidly and the landlord suggested the High Street would shortly be inundated again. The River Tees could be heard roaring in fury as it raced its course through the nearby old stone bridge and once outside after breakfast, my worst fears were confirmed, the bridge was closed to all traffic. Unlike previously, the Watch had been called out and six sturdy men, armed with cudgels, prevented traffic crossing from either direction.

Checking the date with some of the crowd gathered to watch the roaring torrent, I learned it was now Tuesday the 30th May and confirmation of this sent a shiver up my spine. I had forty eight hours maximum to get across and fulfil my obligation.

After all the tremendous effort I had put in over twelve long months, I was in sight of my goal and stopped by the River Tees.

Back at the tavern I ordered a small beer and sat drinking and thinking deeply. There had to be a solution to this problem and it had to be thought out very quickly. What were the difficulties I had to face? First I was carrying a very large and heavy satchel full of £6,000 plus and that made me a clear target for villains. Then the weight of the satchel prevented me walking quickly. Plus the barrier of the River Tees running at its furious pace threatening the stone bridge and alarming the citizens. It was only fourteen years ago that a previous iron bridge had collapsed into the river at this point and there was a distinct nervousness about the security of this old stone bridge now battered by the rushing and turbulent water and for that reason all movement was banned and strictly enforced.

Slowly a plan developed with a high risk element but possibly achievable.

Along the High Street I walked carefully in the rain and water, carrying my satchel until I came to a Bank. I went in and asked if I could open an account and deposit some money. Once again I was viewed with suspicion but once I placed my satchel on the counter, matters improved considerably. The Manager appeared as if by magic and I was ushered into the inner sanctum of his office.

There I explained my predicament and my previous dealings with Bankers in Romford, Huntingdon and Wetherby, producing the receipts I had kept from the previous transactions. Once my story was told and the amount of money was mentioned, he became much engrossed in my welfare, now firmly convinced I was not a common thief.

For a small charge I established an Account, deposited the majority of my money, keeping only £5.0.0d for my immediate use and £1,900 to pay my debt to my Solicitor.

Much lightened now, I slung my satchel over my shoulders and went to reconnoitre the stone bridge over the river.

Fortunately the torrential rain kept the majority of the townsfolk indoors, and being used to the hardship of soaking clothing, I was better placed than most local people to remain outdoors.

Yarm Bridge was a single span over the River Tees with many arches and a rounded semi-circular span on the northern bank of the river and my destination. Viewed from below and each side I noticed there was a very narrow protrusion of about three to four inches all along the upriver face of the bridge.

It was just possible that in the pitch dark I could use the parapet as a support and edge my feet slowly over the whole span. Careful checking showed the protruding ridge went right across the without a break.

Risk taking had been part of my life for some time now but to creep slowly over the raging Tees would be one of my wildest gambles to date.

Could it be done? Mentally I assessed the risks and pitfalls in the knowledge that one false step in the darkness and I would be washed down river with no chance of survival.

But if I bought some black silk gloves to hide my hands and stripped to the bare essentials, I could probably cross that bridge with my lightened satchel and make it to Stockton.

Back to my room at the Ketton Ox, a lunch was taken and I paid the landlord for a further night's stay. Stripped off, I dried myself as best I could and tumbled into bed to sleep as much as possible.

A plan was forming. If the river had not subsided by tomorrow morning, I decided to endeavour to cross that next night.

After a good night's sleep, I dressed my wounds, enjoyed a healthy breakfast and sloshed my way into the High Street and my worst fears were confirmed, rising water and no foreseeable let up. Common sense dictated that I should lie up and rest as much as possible before my ordeal and I gladly did just this.

Heavy pouring rain greeted my awakening at about 11pm and I was thankful that my profession of drover gave me the ability to sleep and rise for duties when the hour commanded. I had collected a little food for sustenance and put this in the satchel with the money.

Dressing took some time. I discarded garments pale or white in colour, sticking to dark clothing, not that I had that much to wear. Despite the wet condition of everything I finally decided to put on, I knew it would look better to appear to be properly clothed otherwise I would be stopped as a vagrant. Surplus clothing was left in the room and about to be abandoned until the thought struck that I could make a realistic looking 'body' from my shirt and the bedclothes and this I did with alacrity.

Lashing rain at the window indicated a rising wind outside which sent further shivers of alarm through me. I was far from fit and still suffering from the wounds taken in my fight with the late Kirk's scoundrels.

At midnight I left my room, crept silently down the wooden stairs in my stocking feet and emerged from the rear of the tavern into a dark yard with water swirling under the locked wooden door. Donning my sturdy boots, I climbed over with my burdens, using what little light prevailed to see by and my heavy heart sank further on hearing the swirling turbulent torrent of water making its noisy way through Yarm to the sea ten miles away. With rising trepidation I realised that could be my destination.

Wading through the water at the edge of the river, I approached the bridge on its western face, very careful of my footing on the slime and spotted six men guarding the crossing, some at the Yarm side, others patrolling nervously over the road bridge below which the stone central pillars broke the rushing waters. These pillars had been shaped in to a vee to cut the water and give protection to the foundations that were at this moment under incredible pressure from the ever rising stream. Wind roared now adding extra menace to the heavy pelting rain, and all I had to do was cross to the other side unnoticed!

Wearing a dark woollen hat and black clothing only my hands and face would be vaguely seen, but I rubbed mud on the latter and wore my black silk gloves on my hands. My satchel was filled with money and some food was slung over my shoulder and I was on my way.

Throughout my journeys across harsh moorland in England and Scotland, I have had occasion to scramble and climb rocky crags to check for robbers and thieves following our drove. I had become adept in recognising all the useful handholds and particularly those places covered in moss and lichen where I would surely slip.

Also I was familiar with the different properties of

various kinds of rock and stone; large grained sandstone was good for example but fine grain stone less so.

Of course it would be pitch black dark. Any light would come from the flaming torches carried by the members of the Watch and if found I would likely be arrested on the spot and that would put paid to my urgent need to cross the river.

I hoped to hang on to the stone parapet and scramble slowly across the west side of the bridge using the small stone ledge I had noticed to get purchase for my booted feet. Before that I had to distract the bridge keepers and the small dummy body I had contrived in my room may well do just that, being so much like a small human being.

Dropping the dummy in the fast running water, I cried in a shrill falsetto, "Help," upon which a bridge keeper ran to the side of the bridge, cried out in alarm and ran back across the structure gathering his fellow keepers and pointing to the bundle now flowing away from the faint light from their lanterns. They crowded to the eastern wall, peering into the darkness and I commenced my perilous escapade, slowly moving away from the light they created and into a murky blackness, water round my feet and pushing my feet along the narrow stone ledge, hanging on for dear life to the stone parapet above. Eventually after an arm-wrenching ordeal, I came to the first of the passing recesses built on top of the pillars that are set out across the bridge supports allowing pedestrians to move off the bridge carriageway and enable horses, carts and coaches to pass safely.

At this place my legs could be spread out across the right angle formed by the bridge and the pillar. All my weight was taken on my feet and my severely aching arms could be allowed to drop briefly and let me regain some control of my shaking muscles. And the strain was terrible. My outdoor life and sturdy frame were now exposed to an awesome task. I was a quarter of the way across and committed to continue this mad venture.

Rounding this obstacle after a suitable rest, I continued my slow creeping way, each foothold having to be felt for on these narrow ledges and then allowing my aching arms to move me a little further, the satchel getting heavier with rain water.

Time stood still for me. The pain now was starting to affect me but I reached the second pedestrian recess and again rested for a longer period before I felt I could successfully manoeuvre round it and commenced the next section.

In exactly the same manner I edged along, feeling with my feet and following with my hands along the parapet stones. It was exhausting.

Lashing rain in the rising wind tugged at my meagre clothing, sending the cold rain water right down my whole body.

Clinging desperately to the parapet, my left foot slipped into space. Steadying myself as best I could, I fought the waves of fear and panic that overcame me and concentrated very hard on survival.

There had to be a continuation of the thin ledge and

with this thought and a hasty prayer I moved my body in an arch and let my left foot creep out to my maximum stretch. Found it! The ledge continued and I racked my body slowly along, allowing my right trailing foot to find the right part of the ledge and in this slow painful manner I reached the next recess where again I spread my weight along my legs, hung my head and panted for a long time to get my breath.

Hands and fingers now raw with clinging to the stone parapet, I desperately needed to relax my arms and get the blood flowing again as they had begun to tremble almost uncontrollably with the massive exertion I was placing on them.

One more pedestrian recess to go. This was the large curve and was the last of the obstacles before the Northern or Egglescliffe bank had to be tackled. My feet and legs were now failing me, my calf muscles trembling almost uncontrollably, and I was hanging by my aching hands to the stone parapet, trying to make my weary legs take a few more steps and inching my way along the wet stones.

My forearms were numb and I could feel my fingers opening up and start to slide over the parapet. I had no reserves left. The end of this climbing foolishness was approaching fast!

Expecting to fall at any moment, I summoned up all my remaining strength and pushed hard with my feet, found purchase and eased my body another foot. I was now close to the river bank below where I could hear the swirling water and paused to again get my breath.

Staring hard through the rain brought no sign of my destination but I sensed the sound of the river was different and risking all, with great effort and pain, I pulled myself over the parapet and on to the road over the bridge.

Staying perfectly still, I listened for signs of the watchkeepers but I was alone. The rain and wind had driven them to the Yarm side of the river.

I crept on my hands and knees the final painful yards and collapsed under the lee of a tree. I wrung as much water out of my clothing and boots as I could, and rested.

By my reckoning it had taken the best part of an hour to cross that accursed stream and after an hour's rest it would now be roughly 2am. In my exhausted state I had to walk almost five miles into Stockton.

Getting slowly to my feet, I took very small consolation that the wind and rain were at my back as I trudged through the muddy carriageway and headed due north.

Walking was in my blood and despite my weariness and terrible now open wounds from exertion, I was able to keep a steady pace, eating the remains of the soaking wet pie found in my satchel which gave me a little more strength, and strangely I had no real problem with a water supply to quench my thirst.

On I trod through the inky blackness, houses and trees lining the streets giving me a sense of direction and I was relieved to see lights glimmering faintly in the distance after leaving the houses and starting a long cold wet walk across saturated roads on the main carriageway.

Previously when I had been on this road, it had been on the back of a racing horse and my recollection of the area was very vague but I knew a long stretch of road gave way to houses on the very outskirts of Stockton.

So it proved, some small lights in windows giving me the guidance I needed to press on, and after another hour, by my reckoning, I came to the wide open thoroughfare that is Stockton-on-Tees High Street and by the clock in the Market Place I was heartily relieved to see it was 4am and it was growing light with dawn. Rain and wind beat down as I made my way to Finkle Street and the premises of Mr Dyson Frobisher in whose sheltered doorway I was found and woken by his alarmed staff when they arrived for work at 8.30am.

Mr Frobisher arrived at 8.45am and was both immensely pleased to see me but incredibly alarmed at my woebegone state.

Thankfully he confirmed my immediate question about the money and advised I had exactly complied with the terms of the contract and he and his chief clerk signed paperwork to that effect.

Questions, tea, food. Doctors administering to my wounds, and finding warm clothing took up the next hour and a half, and it was only when Dyson felt I was in full possession of my faculties that he relieved me of a very soggy bunch of notes to the value of £1,900,0s.0d and gave me a formal signed receipt.

Then his bombshell! Information he had received in confidence led him to believe that at any moment I would receive an offer for my land far in excess of what I had paid. Two prominent businessmen in the town were developing the waterfront for shipping as Yarm, the small town I had just left, was considered too far for the bigger vessels now plying the Tees.

Under no circumstances could I be allowed to leave his office until he had received firm offers and he had given his solemn word that I would not depart his premises. Clothing, a bed, linen, washing and bathing facilities were available upstairs and I was not to leave for seven days.

Countering this shocking discovery was the hint that a very substantial amount of money was being suggested for my interest in the land and it was Dyson's firm belief that he was acting in my best interests here.

CHAPTER 28
LOCKED UP IN STOCKTON

In March 1819 I had entered these premises and gambled a lot of money on this land venture. In one whole year I had bought cattle, moved them hundreds of miles, fought off thieves, robbers, bandits and murderers, endured a harsh winter in Suffolk and was parted from my dear wife for far too long. Then this imprisonment. This was not going to happen.

My enforced incarceration was to prevent either of the contestants for my land making overtures to me in their favour and I could see it from Dyson's point of view, certainly if I was about to say, double my money, but that was not a known fact.

Far more worrying to me was that £4,392.5s.0d was sitting in my Bank in Yarm and I owed £ £4,324.0s.0d on my Letter of Credit in Dumfries due on the 4th June 1820 or I would be declared bankrupt.

Furious at this turn of events, I summoned Dyson Frobisher to my presence and suggested, in very strong terms, that if he wished to retain me as a valued client he would take my instructions and not those of potential purchasers. He saw wisdom. Not only wisdom, he became very concerned that I should doubt he had served my best interests. Then I reminded him of my background and suggested in the strongest possible terms that he would much rather I prosper as a good friend, than make a bad enemy of me.

On that note he humbly agreed that I was correct and he had overstepped the mark.

My bombshell almost finished him off, but brave man, he listened and acted.

Hiring a coach and horses, he despatched his Chief Clerk to Yarm to attempt or force his way across the Tees, visit my Bank and withdraw all my money, some £4,392.5s.0d and bring it back to Stockton as quickly as possible. He prepared correct papers for me to sign and assured me the Bank Manager knew him very well and would recognise his signature and seal.

Dumfries.

My Letter of Credit said payment on the 4th June but did not stipulate a time. After my overnight stay on his Stockton premises, it was now the 2nd June and I was 123 miles from my destination.

We both agreed that the enforced stay was an irrelevance and the whole future riverside transaction was in my hands and my decision only.

Putting our heads together, I realised that using coach and horses it was just possible I could travel the one hundred and twenty three odd miles from Stockton to Dumfries but it would be expensive and a very tight timetable.

But I'll say this, Mr Dyson Frobisher has some very useful connections.

Prominent coach proprietors were clients of his and were summoned to the office and arrived very promptly.

Frank Gardner, for that was the coach proprietor's name, was a common sense typical Yorkshireman in that nothing was too much trouble, subject to money. He knew all the staging posts along my proposed route and his suggestion was that a coach and two were to be preferred as the lighter load meant the horses could move a lot quicker.

My route would be Darlington, Bowes, Brough, Appleby, Penrith, Carlisle, Annan and Dumfries, practically non-stop apart from changes of horses and comfort breaks. There would also be the return journey and he proposed a charge of 3d a mile which at almost two hundred and fifty miles would cost me £5.10s.0d which I had in my pocket from my money brought over the Tees.

I paid him cash and we set about arranging my journey. Nothing could happen until the Chief Clerk came back from Yarm but the rain had ceased and the Tees runs off very quickly so we had high hopes of his prompt return.

Long June days were in my favour, reckoned Frank Gardner, and the coach and horses could travel until very late, provided we had a prompt start. It was now 3pm on the 2nd June and time was running very short for me.

Noise in the street below the office saw the Chief Clerk enter the room triumphant with all my money safe in his custody and a small fee deducted by the bank of £1.0s.0d for the rapid transaction.

Straight outside then and with all my money back in my satchel and clothed only in borrowed attire I set off on my long journey.

The towns seemed to race by although the post boy, an aged but wise man, in fact maintained a good steady pace, never tiring the horses, and Frank Gardner had agreed we would change steeds every fifteen miles to maintain pace and not tire the animals too much.

In this way we traversed the country and by 10.30pm approximately we came to a stop in Darlington for an overnight stay. Using a tavern recommended by the post boy, I had a sleep until woken at 4am and was advised, "We should get going again, sir," the post boy having been warned to wake me.

Away promptly and with fresh horses, we galloped and trotted our way across the northern carriageways. Forty five miles and many stops saw us approaching Brough and my heart longed to see familiar faces but only Hector appeared at the coach changing station. Delighted as he was to see me, I couldn't stop very long but asked him to contact Giselle and tell her I would be coming back through Brough in four or five days and could she meet me please.

We made Carlisle that night and the post boy and I almost fell into the resting house and into a dreamless sleep with me resting on my precious satchel to keep it safe.

I had expected trouble on the road and carried my dirk

in my pocket. I missed the company of George Cook and that great big wolfhound but there was nothing happening and my vigilance was deemed unnecessary by the post boy who reckoned we were travelling too fast for news of our venture to have spread to the robbers and highwaymen. That said, I noticed he carried a huge loaded blunderbuss under the seat.

Next morning saw us washing and having breakfast at 4.30am with first light and we started again with fresh horses from the ostlers for the long stretch to Dumfries.

Annan came at about noon where we again changed horses for the final stretch.

Dumfries changes little and we arrived there at 6pm. After a brisk journey and meeting little or no traffic, we pulled up dusty, tired and very thirsty and straight in to the Grapes Inn where I had arranged to meet and redeem my Letter of Credit.

There was nobody in the bar that I remembered. Then I realised that it was 6pm and they would have assumed the worst. Questions to the landlord confirmed my suspicions and a very angry farmer had left at 4pm threatening to skin me alive once he found me!

Now the farming community lived rather frugally in those parts and I recalled they much preferred to stay in rather primitive accommodation on the outskirts of town. So after a quick slake of our thirst, the post boy and I took our by now very tired horses and slowly reached the outskirts and the farmers' tavern.

Never has a man been greeted so cheerfully by a thankful

farmer as I was that late June evening. I reckoned I could have stayed there for a week they were so overjoyed.

Drinks served and thirst quenched, we both repaired to the room at the rear of the inn used for these transactions. I asked him to produce my Letter of Credit which he did, although you could hardly recognise it, being so creased and thumbed but sure enough it was the document I wanted.

Taking my satchel, I counted out in £1 notes an amount of £4,324.0s.0d and watched fascinated as the money was eyed by the boisterous farmer with tears running down his cheeks.

He explained that for one full year he had struggled to keep his head above water, pay his debts and live as frugally as he possibly could. From all sides he had been called a fool and a dolt for entrusting so many cattle to a relatively unknown young drover and his standing and credit in his hometown stood at nothing.

Indeed it had been suggested that it was a complete waste of his time and a long journey to find I had disappeared never to be seen again. My failure to arrive was the last straw and he was about to sell his land to jeering men who had followed him down sensing a handsome profit from his demise.

Cheeks dried and small beers on the table, the tales of my trip to England gave him long thought and when we finished talking, he shook my hand, gave me back my Letter of Credit which I destroyed and burnt and we parted on very good terms with my reputation intact.

Back on our weary way into Dumfries, we settled the horses with some ostlers the post boy knew and I invited him to join me for dinner before we slept soundly till 7am when the whole process started in reverse but this time without any time constraints. We covered ground steadily through Annan, Carlisle and to Penrith where we spent the second night.

I had suggested to Hector, the coachman, that Giselle should be aware we might be coming through Brough on the 7th June and we arrived at about 4pm.

There, waiting for me with a smile from heaven was my wife, Jeremiah and Henrietta Ridley, Dag my wolfhound and a pram.

Huge hugs and kisses from Giselle made me feel simply dumbstruck. I couldn't believe this beautiful girl was my wife and I must admit a tear or two fell.

Holding each other very tight, I greeted Mr and Mrs Ridley and then I saw my parents rushing over. Mother cried and hugged me, Dad shook hands and then embraced me, Dag wagged his tail as though it would come off and then a baby cried. Amazed beyond belief, I stared at the pram, hardly daring to believe it was true. I was the immensely proud Father of a bouncing baby boy.

Holding him in my arms for the first time was a feeling only a new Father can appreciate and when he gurgled at me, my face must have been a picture. Everybody laughed with delight.

Then the post boy coughed loudly and reminded me of my obligation.

Still holding Giselle close and carrying my baby boy in my arms, I explained that I had to leave immediately to fulfil a promise to my Solicitor to return to his office at the earliest possible moment to conclude the possible sale of the land I had purchased.

Giselle asked about the deal and I told her that an offer was forthcoming which might see me make a modest profit on the investment.

Her news, whispered in my ear, was that Jeremiah and Henrietta Ridley had received an offer for Ridley House and all its land and they wondered if Giselle and I would be able to match it.

CHAPTER 29
ESCAPE, DEBTS PAID, FIGHT TO THE FINISH

It broke my heart to explain to Giselle that the wondrous deal I had negotiated in Stockton for the riverside land was now looking like only a moderate success and I had to return there immediately and conclude on the best terms I could and get out.

Clinging to me very tightly, she said, "I understand perfectly that you have to return and finalise but what is important now is that you come back to us all safe and sound and don't take any risks."

Knowing as I did the situation in Stockton, it was difficult to keep from blurting out that the offer I hoped to get would release about £2000 plus for our use and little more.

I kissed Giselle very fondly, kissed my as yet un-named son, caressed Henrietta and Mum, shook hands with Dad and Jeremiah, and at the prompting of the post boy Albert we set off for Stockton again with fresh horses and in my case a very heavy heart.

Two days hard travelling saw us on the outskirts of

Stockton and by early afternoon I presented myself at the offices of Mr Dyson Frobisher.

Immediately I sensed a very changed atmosphere and nervousness in the staff. The clerk that greeted me was subdued and the Chief Clerk, in taking me to Dyson's office, spoke not a word. On entering the main office it became immediately obvious that Dyson had been very badly beaten.

He nursed a broken arm in a very new sling, had cuts on his hand and a very black eye.

Sitting down opposite, I waited for his explanation which was awesome in its implications.

Two parties were anxious to buy my land but one had taken the step of sending ruffians to beat Dyson up and promised that the same punishment awaited me if I did not agree to the sale of my land to this particular party. What was more, they were on the look out for me and would meet out a similar beating at the first opportunity.

Red mists came over me again. It was some time before I could speak and I then made it clear how very sorry I was that Dyson had ended up being so terribly mauled on my behalf.

Half an hour of questioning and I knew roughly the probable whereabouts of these villains who were three in number, two large fat men and a skinny youth who had guided them to Dyson's office. He was a known pickpocket and sneak thief living by his wits.

No price had been indicated by either party for the land I had for sale so I had no idea if I was about to show a profit for all my efforts. I was filled with a cold fury and abruptly left the office but not before the staff warned me not to go into the cellar. The door was firmly locked as that whole part of the building had flooded to a depth of at least five feet and this on the same day that Dyson was molested and beaten. No wonder the staff looked woebegone.

Having an idea building in my mind, I backtracked to the coach yard and after enquiry found Albert the post boy. Albert Atkins was his name and he had proved a very worthy companion in our long travel across country, agile, wily, fit and handy with his fists. I reckoned he could give me a hand with my next venture and be paid for doing so.

Speaking to Frank Gardner, I obtained his permission to approach Albert and once I explained my mission, and the cash I would offer, he jumped at the chance to join me but suggested a more modest sum of money would suffice.

Sure enough Albert knew about the pickpocket and his likely whereabouts so we went hunting. In the filthy smoke-filled back streets of Stockton we did not stand out as I had adopted a very scruffy image at Albert's suggestion. He just stayed the same.

Finding a general store I went in, checked the goods for sale and purchased a very large hessian net, to Albert's surprise, plus two heavy woollen socks. Once outside we strode away out of earshot of passers-by and I explained my intentions which met with immediate approval and excitement.

Hiding our purchases in a dingy building nearby, we set about stalking the pickpocket. I'm good at this but Albert was my equal and we traced the lad and waited until he was alone, counting his pilfered goods when we overpowered him and took him to the place we had stored the net.

Inside I broke both of his wrists with a stick before I asked any questions. Albert was somewhat taken aback at this but it proved a good tactic.

Mr Pickpocket would not work again for many months and would disappear quickly once I released him.

Questioned about his accomplices, he eventually gave us their descriptions but more importantly their immediate location. His orders given in a note were to take the men to the Solicitors' office where they would act in a heavy handed way but would not inflict any damage. They had overstepped the mark but the unknown instigator had paid the men handsomely and they were mighty drunk in a tavern nearby on the edge of the River Tees. But he had no knowledge of the perpetrator and only the ruffians knew this.

I kicked him, wailing loudly, out of the dirty building we were using and he scampered away without a backward glance.

Albert and I waited for darkness to fall and that late June night it took its time to become dark, but eventually it did and we moved quietly to the tavern mentioned and the row and noise from inside indicated we had the right place.

Creeping up to the window, I looked inside and there

were our suspects, singing loudly, banging the table and demanding more drinks from a very nervous landlord. As I watched, the few people left inside were making preparations to leave.

Above the back door of the rear exit was a small porch jutting out about three feet and it looked secure. At my suggestion, Albert shinned up the drainpipe nearby and stood on the roof now holding my large hessian sack.

I filled each of the socks with mud which was available in quantities after the heavy rain, so effectively I had two weighty coshes to subdue and render unconscious any body unwise enough to be in reach.

During my time in Scotland I had seen the hessian net used to great effect when dropped on unsuspecting persons. There was the tendency to fight the thing whereas the correct way was to drop to the ground, raise an edge and attempt an escape.

Albert indicated he was ready and I entered the tavern which had now emptied apart from my victims and the scared landlord.

These were two very big men who I would have avoided tackling individually, never mind together, but my plan was based on boldness or stupidity, depending on your point of view.

Moving quickly to the table the men shared, I nodded as though we were acquainted, bent down as with the intention to speak to them and as they lowered their heads, I bashed them together very forcefully, stood and walked out.

It took thirty seconds for them to react but then two bull-like roars went up and they charged for the rear exit as planned.

Timing, when correct, is a wonderful thing to behold and Albert had it absolutely right. As they cleared the door, the large net enveloped them from above and in the dark yard they fought a furious battle with the net and each over, shouting, cursing, tripping, falling, all exactly as planned.

Letting them tire themselves at the fruitless task, I moved in at the right moment and caught each one on the back of the neck with my weighted sock. Down they went, unconscious and tangled in netting.

Albert came down, looking very impressed in the light from the tavern and we removed with difficulty these two strapping men from the netting's embrace, then tied their thumbs very tightly behind their backs and roped their feet.

A delighted landlord then joined us with many thanks and Albert asked if he still used a wheelbarrow for moving casks of ale about. With a positive answer, we borrowed it and with some difficulty loaded the two unconscious forms, assisted with gusto by the landlord.

Through the dark streets we wheeled the forms, meeting not a soul and in a short time we reached the Solicitiors' premises in Finkle Street to carry out the second part of my plan. Albert was unaware of my intentions but took an active interested part in proceedings, his eyes widening when he realised just what I had in mind.

Like many offices the cellars were never visited, being so damp that documents could not be stored safely. So the door was always locked but the key was traditionally left on a nail somewhere in the vicinity and I was relying on this.

Searching the most likely places, I located a key which fitted the substantial lock, undid the door, stood back and allowed Albert to come closer onto the steps where I lifted the ruffians out of the barrow and dragged them through the cold water and placed them in a corner. They promptly came round with water up to their chests and the bitter cold steeping into their drunken frames.

Just out of interest, I asked if they could remember the name of the man that had paid them to assault my good friend, Mr Frobisher, the Solicitor. Anglo Saxon words were uttered. So I said goodbye and locked the door behind me, leaving them to gently soak in freezing muddy water.

Both Albert and I were very tired and he knew of a decent tavern we could still get access to as it was used by coaching people. I agreed, subject to me meeting all the costs and off we went for a good night's sleep and a hearty breakfast.

Nine o'clock saw me back at the Solicitors' office where I was met with curious stares. Noises had been heard from the cellar but all were afraid to venture near. I explained to Dyson Frobisher just what steps I had taken and asked him to contact a fellow member of the legal profession who would be a reliable person in court.

About 9.30am I took the key from my pocket and went down the stairs to the cellar where I waded and opened the door. The stench alone was unbearable, both men looked deathly pale and all fight and bravado had left them.

My terms, as I explained to them, were quite simple. The name of their paymaster given to two Solicitors to witness and both be then taken to the Court House where charges of assault would be levelled at them and they would be placed in gaol. Alternatively they could just wait a little longer if that's what they would prefer. Through chattering teeth, they begged me to bring the Solicitors to them immediately before they succumbed to the cold.

Dyson Frobisher and his companion carried notebooks as they came down the cellar stairs to the open doorway and were visibly shocked at what they saw, but Dyson shrugged, remembered his savage beating at their hands and took an immediate statement which his colleague noted in his book.

Our culprit was a well-known shifty businessman and within two hours he was found by the Magistrate's men and locked up in the Town Gaol to await his fate.

That problem solved, I asked Dyson to bring me up to date with any offers he had received for my land and he asked me to come to his office. There, over a cup of tea he explained he had an offer now, in writing, of £6,000.0s.0d for my land and he recommended I should accept it which I did. To be perfectly honest I was almost lost for words, the £6,000 went through my head followed by the realisation that I could achieve my ambition and buy Ridley Hall. Dyson Frobisher could yet be a very busy boy.

Payment was to be instant in cash and an agreement was drawn up that very afternoon, suitably witnessed, and I left that office, having settled my account, with more personal money than I had known in my short life. I made a written note to remind me I owed George Cook half of the monies earned on the drove. That would be a long evening with the odd beer.

Albert Atkins and I had got along very well. I liked the man despite his rough appearance and wily ways, plus I felt he would be a very useful man to have around as I moved from droving to possibly farming.

With this in mind, I called and spoke to Frank Gardner and asked if he could consider releasing Albert from his employment so he could work for me. Quite a long time elapsed after that request. Frank looked at me long and hard, asking just what I had in mind, then I explained about my changed circumstances and need for a reliable foreman to act on my behalf and grow any enterprise I developed. Reassured that Albert was to be a permanent employee, he gave his grudging acceptance but on the understanding that Albert must want to move away to Brough.

That obstacle over, I approached Albert with my proposition and offer and we discussed this for a long time. He was happily married and living in rented accommodation with his wife and two children and they would have to be consulted.

Wages were discussed and I agreed to pay him the handsome sum of £2.10s.0d per week which I did right then.

That was the key. His face lit up, he raced home and within the hour was back and I had a foreman.

Testing his newfound status, he was asked to acquire a horse and carriage for my journey to Brough which he did with alacrity and at a price far lower than I expected. Then I stated the horse and carriage were for him to use to bring his family over to Brough within the week. For my part, could he now get me a place on the next coach and four that was heading in the direction of Brough?

CHAPTER 30
RETURN TO BROUGH

Anticipation can make a long journey pass in short order as imagination takes over and the welcome is almost written before arrival.

Nothing could compare to dismounting in Brough, hiring a horse and riding very quickly the short one and a half miles to Ridley Hall on the northern outskirts of the town.

Nearing the big house I admired its fine location, the surrounding fields of pasture and the sweeping drive to the front door.

Somebody must have passed a warning, for the front door was flung open and the most gorgeous girl in the world ran towards me and flew into my arms with a huge leap as I dismounted from my horse.

Giselle and I embraced for long moments, or rather she allowed me to come slowly down to Earth, and then I explained our good fortune with the land sale in Stockton. £6,000.0s.0d.

She was incredulous, completely taken aback.

"Jack, that means we can buy Ridley House. They

want £1,200.0s.0d for it with 72 acres and it's perfect for us."

Looking round, I could only agree as I took in the improvements since I was last here, fenced fields in good order, typical drove cattle ground for an overnight stance plus drover accommodation: all the signs of a regular busy location, such as I had seen up and down the country.

"Where's our son?" I said, slowly disentangling myself from her arms, with some reluctance."

Giselle said, "Giles is with your Mother in the house. Your Mother and Father live here now. While you have been wandering through England and Scotland, I've organised fortnightly soirees for the local gentry who all enjoy the craze for tea and wish to know my source! Jeremiah and Hetty thought the idea was brilliant and it has proved popular and very profitable. But you must come inside and have a cup of tea and we'll bring you up to date, but I can't tell you how glad I am to have you back, my Jack."

Indoors it was all explained. The tea soirees had been so popular that both Jeremiah and Hetty were overwhelmed with the number of guests, and Giselle asked George and Mary, my parents, if they could help which they did.

Giselle explained, "We have had such a busy time and the house we were going to use was empty so I asked George and Mary to help out and move in. They love it!"

As they spoke, I nursed a bright eyed baby on my knee and found myself completely enraptured with him, dark eyes, chubby face and gripping my finger with his little hands. I was almost in tears. Giles, what a lovely name, I thought, and maintaining that French connection too.

Back again to the family and friends I loved, not only had they developed a very healthy business but from passing drovers Giselle bought all the knitted goods that they traditionally produced as they walked. She then sold them in the local Brough Market and in Kirby Stephen which brought in a good profit.

Hetty Ridley, it appeared, had blossomed into the welcoming hostess of the soiree. Jeremiah was on hand to administer tea with Mother and Father, who ran the kitchen also and the increasing farm interests which I'd noted on arrival. Father was in his element.

Catching Jeremiah's eye I asked if he would join me in the drawing room out of sight of everybody and once seated I asked if I could buy Ridley Hall for £1200.0s.0d and he agreed with a huge smile.

Returning to the embrace of my family and friends, I quietly explained to a delighted Giselle just what I had done and was greeted with a hug, a kiss and a, "Thank you, Jack," followed swiftly by, "And that damned great dog of yours arrived yesterday and is looking all over for you. Please keep him clean!"

BIBLIOGRAPHY

Bonser, K. J. *The Drovers. Who they were and how they went. An Epic of the English Countryside.*

Brown, Cynthia. Drovers, Cattle and Dung. *The Long Road from Scotland.*

Cumbria Rural Development Programme. *The Droving Tradition of the Upper Eden Valley.*

East Cumbria Countryside Project. *Brough. Exploring its History.*

Haldane, A.R.B. *The Drove Roads of Scotland.*

Hindle, Brian Paul. *Roads and Trackways of the Lake District.*

Kirby Stephen Town Forum. *Drove Ways around Tan Hill.*

Mallerstang Highway Droving Route.

MacDonald, Fraser George. *The Steel Bonnets.*

Roebuck, Peter. *Cattle Droving through Cumbria. 1600-1900.*

With kind assistance.

Cafe Briscoe's. Finkle Street, Stockton-on-Tees.

Dr. Reed Gamble. Chop Gate.

John Coleman. Butcher. Sudbury, Suffolk.

Ashley Coote and Gary Addison. White Horse. Sudbury. Suffolk.

Mrs. Alison Burgess. Dumfries and Galloway Library Service.

Sylvia. M. Kelly. Kendal Library Service.

Martin and Brian Cook.